The Concise Ocean Navigator Guide

A STUDY AND REVISION AID
FOR THE RYA SHORE-BASED
OCEAN YACHTMASTER COURSE,
complete with exercises and test questions

Mike Bowyer

David & Charles

This book is dedicated to my children:
Diana, Catherine, Philip, Sarah, Judith and John,
and also to the many friends I have met and sailed
with in the Reading Offshore Club.

A catalogue record for this book is
available from the British Library.

ISBN 0-7153-0059-8

© Mike Bowyer 1993
First Published 1993

The right of the author to be identified as author of this
work has been asserted by him in accordance with the
Copyright, Designs and Patents Act 1988.

Typeset by Creative Publicity Consultants
Printed by Redwood Books Ltd for David & Charles,
Brunel House, Newton Abbot, Devon.

The Course

The aim of this book is to prepare the ocean yacht navigator for the Royal Yachting Association's Ocean shore based examination. It also hopes to show the reader that if all electronic systems fail, it is possible to navigate in the oceans simply by using a sextant, a chronometer and a nautical almanac. *Reed's* is necessary for the trigonometrical tables - or you can use *Nories'* or *Burton's*.

The other method shown is to use the sextant and chronometer in conjunction with a nautical almanac and the *Sight Reduction Tables for Air Navigation (AP 3270)* HMSO. It is, however, possible to navigate accurately with just three items:

> Sextant
> Chronometer
> *Reed's* nautical almanac

Also on the market are calculators which can be used in conjunction with *Macmillan's* nautical almanac. However, this method is not shown or explained in this book.

The successful completion of a shore based course should give you confidence to try your new skills in practice. In time you may wish to seek the award of the practical certificate, details of which are available from the RYA.

Acknowledgements

The tables and certain illustrations reproduced in this book taken from *Reed's Nautical Almanac* by kind permission of the publishers; and from the *Air Navigation Tables* and *Admiralty Pilots* by kind permission of Her Majesty's Stationery Office.

The Author

Mike Bowyer first went to sea as an apprentice in the Merchant Navy in 1947. He gained his Master's Foreign Going Certificate and was a navigating officer with the Union Castle Mail S.S. Co Ltd until 1962, when he left the sea to pursue a new career in teaching.

Now Deputy Head of a special school in the South of England, one of his many duties is introducing young people to the experience of sailing. As an Instructor for the RYA/DTp shore based Yachtmaster courses (both Offshore and Ocean) for over twenty years he has also introduced many adults to the sea.

Mike kept an Achilles 24 in Cornwall, which he sailed with his wife and young son, but he now sails a Compromis 777 with a mooring on the Hamble River. He has also cruised in the English Channel, Scottish waters and the Mediterranean.

Contents

1
OCEAN CRUISING

Once out of sight of land, the whole nature of being at sea in a small boat changes dramatically. No longer can you say to your crew, 'In a few hours we will reach Cherbourg', or some other favourite port on the French or British coast about twelve hours sailing from your home port. Instead there are days, or possibly weeks, of sailing before you without the familiar worries of tides, crossing the shipping lanes and 'When are we going to get there?'.

So, what is going to happen when you head your boat west to south-west out of the English Channel towards the West Indies, or on a more southerly course down to the Canaries or the Azores? The wind and the waves will be ever-present for many days. You will be able to enjoy starry nights. The heavens are that much more vivid at night in the open ocean. While on watch you will come to recognise stars and planets as they follow their own tracks through the night sky; no doubt one or two will become your particular friends, to be used to plot your position, or to steer by. By day the Sun will become your companion, giving dawn and dusk a whole new meaning.

As you travel southwards the way of sailing begins to change: from being encased in 'oilies' day in and day out whilst in the English Channel, once clear of the Bay of Biscay you can begin to discard them. As you are bowling along in the North East Trade Winds, with the sea extraordinarily blue, you can begin to feel a change from your normal sailing in the grey-green waters of the English Channel.

6

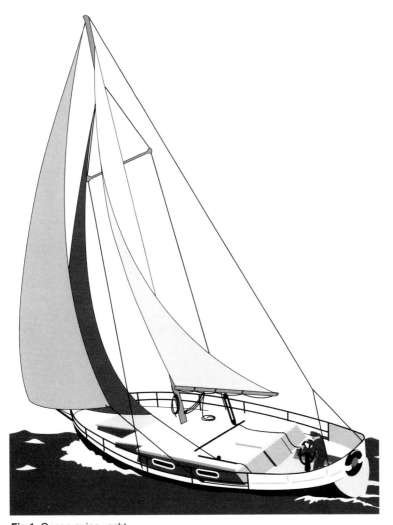

Fig 1 Ocean-going yacht

Preparation

Your intended passage needs to be carefully thought out and planned. You should consider the seaworthiness of the boat, consult all the charts that you will need, study the weather conditions and ocean currents, provision the boat adequately and feel confident that your crew is up to making the passage. A study of the *Admiralty Routeing Charts* will give you a good idea of what winds to expect and when, areas of high and low pressure, the main shipping routes and the ocean currents that will be encountered.

Sailing in Convoy

It is supportive, when ocean sailing, to find other yachts doing the same thing; it is quite common to find a group of yachts planning to sail together on the same ocean passage. Although it is unlikely that they will be in sight of each other they will be in radio contact. If any problem arises there will be yachts close by to give a helping hand. It can give crew a psychological boost to know that nearby there is another yacht going the same way.

It is common practice for a group of yachts to assemble in the Azores or Canaries in November and December so that they are ready to sail to avoid the hurricane season in the West Indies. Up to two hundred boats may gather together to do this. There is great comradeship in ocean sailing and you will make many new friends.

Responsibilities of the Skipper

Before taking a small boat on an ocean passage, the skipper needs to have had some years of sailing experience in coastal waters. Ideally, you will have gained the Royal Yachting Association's Yachtmaster certificate which will have helped to make you confident in boat handling, knowledgeable in meteorology, navigation and the rules of the road. You will also have gained knowledge about all the bits and pieces you need to know on taking a small boat to sea, such as being aware of all the safety equipment you should have on board and how to use it. It is also important to have knowledge and practical experience of electronic equipment, as well as knowing how to use the sextant accurately to obtain a position.

The skipper needs to know that his boat is seaworthy and able to make the intended passage. This might entail strengthening the rigging, a new set of sails and perhaps extra sails, fitting a strong self-steering system and a sizeable ocean radio transmitter and receiver. It would also be wise to make sure that your engine has had a recent overhaul. You will need to provision your vessel adequately and to make sure that you carry enough water.

The skipper must choose the crew with great care: many passages have been spoilt by having the wrong person on board! The skipper needs to spell out to the crew exactly what is involved in the passage and what will be expected of them. Of course, another competent watch-keeper will be essential to the skipper, and the more experienced the crew the safer the passage will be.

Carrying of Firearms

This subject has been aired many times and remains an intensely debated issue. The author once had on his Ocean course a yachtsman who sailed his boat across to the West Indies only to be murdered by a member of the crew of a freighter anchored nearby. His crew, who were unarmed, had to swim, naked and injured, half a mile to the shore following the attack by a knife-wielding man in the middle of the night.

Medical Knowledge

You will be away from any immediate medical assistance. Ocean cruising is all about self-reliance. Consequently, the skipper should have some basic medical knowledge and be able to deal with minor injuries and recognise when someone's condition is potentially serious.

Awareness of Dangers

Ocean sailing is not without its own dangers. A skipper must be alert at all times in case important decisions concerning the safety of the boat have to be made. A strengthening wind may entail reduction of sail, and poor visibility may be a reason for increasing lookouts during the watch.

Whales are a notorious hazard and many yachts have come to grief or had close shaves, thus calling for very special coolness and reassurance of the crew. Objects that have fallen off vessels, including whole containers, large logs and other debris, float around in the oceans. These are impossible to see at night but are quite capable of holing a yacht.

The hurricane season has to be watched, as does the path of every tropical revolving storm. These will sink a yacht and make any rescue almost impossible. Knowledge of tropical revolving storms and their paths is essential.

Landfall

After many days at sea, landfall is always a very exciting moment. It was certainly the case in the days of sail, when a lookout was posted in the crow's nest to spot the land. The call of 'Land ho!' was always welcomed. All crews at sea experience the same feelings of anticipation when arriving at any port in the hope that a safe haven has been reached, even many crews only crossing the English Channel to France.

It is important that the skipper knows the position of the vessel when closing land, and particularly when approaching a port for the first time. Careful attention must be paid to any out-lying dangers and to the effects of any tides or local conditions which govern the approach to a port. Studying the local pilots is important, as is radioing in to the port to give your ETA (Estimated Time of Arrival) and any special requirements that you might have. Make sure that you study the coastal charts carefully and note any useful navigational aids which will help you make a safe entry. Don't forget to make notes and sketches in the logbook which will help when you make a return visit.

2
THE SOLAR SYSTEM

The solar system consists of the Sun and the following planets in the order in which they orbit the Sun, nearest first: Mercury; Venus; Earth; Mars; Jupiter; Saturn; Uranus; Neptune; Pluto. The planetary system consists of the Sun and nine planets and their attendant moons. The Earth, as we know, has one moon while Jupiter and Saturn each have nine.

For ocean navigation purposes we use the Sun, Venus, Mars, Jupiter and Saturn. The Moon is also used, but is less useful, as will be demonstrated later.

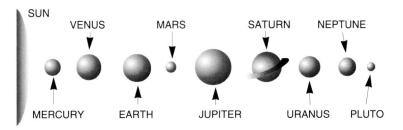

Fig 2 Solar system

The Movements of the Sun

Although the Earth is revolving round the Sun and spinning on its own axis, it is useful in celestial navigation to try and understand the apparent movement of the Sun which we see every day. The Sun apparently rises in the east and sets in the west. This movement is due to the rotation of the Earth on its axis.

The Sun has another apparent movement, which is a north-south and south-north direction. This movement gives us the seasons and is due to the Earth revolving round the Sun. The Earth rotates round the Sun inclined at an angle of $66\frac{1}{2}°$ to its own orbit.

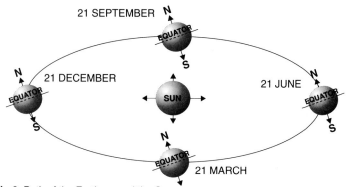

Fig 3 Path of the Earth around the Sun

Apparent Movement of the Sun

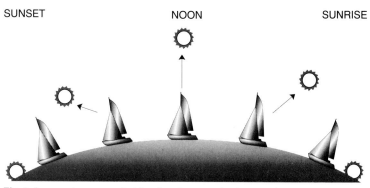

Fig 4 Apparent movement of the Sun from sunrise to sunset

We have to consider the apparent movement of the Sun. The Sun is the easiest heavenly body to use for celestial navigation. It can easily be seen, and even on a cloudy day it will shine through some clouds so that a fix may be obtained. When visible, the Sun will give the navigator a longitude in the morning and after-noon and a latitude at noon each day, so that it is perfectly pos-sible to navigate a vessel across the oceans using only the Sun to obtain a position. The observations taken of the Sun in this manner provide a running fix in exactly the same way a running fix is obtained from the same object when coastal sailing. For small boat sailors, using the Sun has the added advantage in that it can be brought down to the horizon more easily than any other heavenly body. The Sun can further be used at sunset and sunrise to check your compass. This is done by taking a compass bearing of the Sun and comparing it with the true bearing of the Sun, found in the nautical tables under the heading Amplitude Tables.

The compass can also be checked at the time of taking the morning and evening sights if a compass bearing is taken at the same time as taking the sextant altitude of the Sun. The true bearing of the Sun at these times can be found in the nautical almanac under the heading of the ABC Tables.

The Use of the Planets and their Movements

As already mentioned, the following four planets can be used for celestial navigation: Venus, Mars, Jupiter and Saturn. Information for these planets is tabulated in the nautical almanacs on a daily basis. Positions can be obtained using the planets in conjunction with the stars or the Sun.

It is possible, with a good sextant, to use the Sun and a planet to get a fix during daylight hours, particularly if Venus, the brightest of the planets, is used. Towards the end of January 1990 Venus appeared as a morning planet, and could be seen until mid-September; it then became an evening planet from mid-December.

The next brightest is Jupiter and if Jupiter is in the right position in the sky relative to the Sun, ie not too close, a good fix can be obtained. Although Saturn may be visible it, like Jupiter, can sometimes be too close to the Sun for observation. In 1990 Mars could be seen all year as a morning planet, and in November also became visible all night.

The planets are easily recognisable in the night sky as they are brighter than the stars and do not twinkle. Mars has a reddish look about it.

The nautical almanacs indicate the position of the planets, with captions such as 'well placed in the east after sunset'. The planets have their own movements, rising and setting in the same manner as the Sun. But their north-south movements are not nearly so evident as the Sun's. In a year Jupiter's movements (declination) varies by only about five degrees.

The Moon and its Movement

Although the Moon is tabulated in the nautical almanacs, its general speed of movement makes it more difficult to use to gain an accurate position. In one month the declination of the Moon varies by at least sixty-five degrees, so that extreme accuracy is required. Also, because of the visibility of the Moon, you are not able to see the entire lower limb or upper limb (top and bottom circumferance) at certain phases, and it is really only at Full Moon that you can get a limb down to the horizon.

The Moon should only be used in celestial navigation if you have not had a position for some time, and you are able to check your position by some other means within a short time.

The Use of the Sun in Ocean Navigation

As has been indicated earlier, the Sun is the most useful body to use when navigating a small boat across the oceans. It can be used in several ways: to check the error on the compass, to find latitude and to find longitude.

During a day at sea, if the Sun is visible all day, the navigator can begin at sunrise with an amplitude to check the compass.

At about 0800 a sextant altitude of the Sun can be taken to give a longitude. This, in fact, will only give a true longitude if the Sun is bearing east, but nevertheless will give you a position line which you can use as running fix with a run to noon. At noon a sextant altitude of the Sun will give you a latitude and, with the run and transferred position line from the morning sight, a position at noon.

At about 1600 the navigator can take another sextant altitude of the Sun to check the longitude and, finally, an amplitude again at sunset to check the compass. In this way the vessel can be navigated safely across the oceans.

Taking a Sextant Altitude

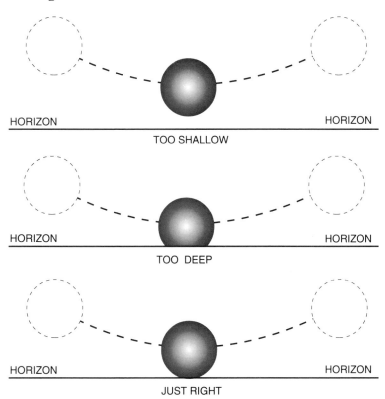

Fig 5 Rocking the sextant

When taking a sextant altitude of the Sun, it is important to make sure that the lower limb of the Sun is just kissing the horizon when you read off the altitude on the sextant. This is achieved by rocking the sextant so that the lower limb is swung to and fro along the horizon to get a good fix. (It is easier to do this with the lower limb.) When using the Sun to find longitude in the morning and afternoon, it is important to choose the moment when you think that you have a good contact with the horizon. Do not forget to use the shades on the sextant to prevent the glare getting to your eyes.

At noon you are watching for the maximum altitude the Sun

will reach that day. You should be able to spot this fairly easily. While you are watching the Sun through the telescope on your sextant, the Sun will still be rising and you will have to keep winding the micrometer screw to keep it on the horizon. When it reaches its maximum altitude it appears to stop for a short time before the lower limb is seen below the horizon. A latitude is obtained when you see that the Sun has stopped rising.

To make sure that the correct altitude was being obtained, it was not uncommon, in the earlier days of shipping, for two or three navigating officers and the captain to use their sextants to 'shoot' the Sun at noon and to use a mean reading from their sextants to get as accurate a latitude as possible.

When taking sights at 0800 or 1600, it is advisable to take two or three in succession and take the mean of your results in your final calculations. You will sometimes feel that you have taken a good sight, and maybe your judgement is correct.

If for some reason clouds covered the Sun at noon or it was foreseen that by noon it would be overcast, then a latitude could still be obtained about half an hour either side of noon by using some nautical tables called *Ex-Meridian Tables*. This means 'outside', or 'after' or 'before', the Sun is on the meridian. The Sun is said to be on your meridian at noon, when it has reached its maximum altitude for that day and it is bearing due south or north. A meridian altitude is the term used for finding the altitude of the Sun at noon, to give you your latitude.

Definitions of the Sun's Movements

Greenwich Hour Angle (GHA) The Sun's apparent east to west movement is calculated daily in the nautical almanacs and comes under the heading of GHA, Greenwich Hour Angle. It is the amount, in degrees, that the Sun is west of Greenwich for any particular time of the day. In twenty-four hours the Sun will go from a GHA of 0° at 1200 hours to 60° at about 1600 hours, to 180° at midnight, to 270° at about 0600 the next day, to 315° at about 0900, and so to 360° at midday the next day, so covering the full twenty-four hours.

Declination The Sun's apparent north and south movement is called declination. The Sun's declination will be north or south depending on the time of the year. The Sun will reach a maximum declination of $23\frac{1}{2}°$ north on or about 21 June each year, to reach the Tropic of Cancer, and will then return south to reach a maximum declination of about twenty-three and a half degrees south on or about 21 December, to reach the Tropic of Capricorn.

The Sun's declination will be $0°$ on or about 21 March and 21 September. These are called the Equinoxes. At these times, all places on the surface of the Earth have equal lengths of night and day.

On the celestial sphere, declination is the latitude of the Sun, and Greenwich Hour Angle measured west from Greenwich is the longitude of the Sun. So the celestial position of the Sun can be found for every hour, minute and second of the day. This information is tabulated daily in the nautical almanacs.

Nautical Almanacs

Information about the Sun can be found in *Macmillan's*, *Reed's* and *Admiralty* nautical almanacs. In *Reed's* and the *Admiralty* almanacs the declination and Greenwich Hour Angle of the Sun is given for each hour of the day, with a correction table for minutes and seconds. In *Macmillan's* the same information is given on a daily basis with correction tables for hours, minutes and seconds. In *Reed's* there is a pull-out table for the corrections, while the correction table in the *Admiralty* almanac is at the back of the book. Times of sunset and sunrise are given, as well as times of civil and nautical twilight. Times of moonrise and moonset are given, as well as the phases of the Moon. There is also information on planets, with the times of Greenwich Hour Angle and declination for Venus, Mars, Jupiter and Saturn. A table of selected stars is given, with all their respective magnitudes, hour angles and declinations. A separate table is given for using the star Polaris.

The ocean navigator needs to become familiar with a nautical almanac so that use of the tables can be carried out at sea easily and with as little error as possible. For further details about the different almanacs and tables please see Chapter 17. Examples of these tables can be found in the Appendix.

3

THE CELESTIAL SPHERE

In celestial navigation it is useful to try and imagine a sphere which surrounds the Earth. On this sphere are the Sun, stars, planets and moons, which are fixed on the inside surface of the sphere an infinite distance away from the Earth. Perhaps an easier vision of the celestial sphere would be as a large bubble with the Earth as a pin-prick at its centre and all the heavenly bodies attached to the inside surface. If you are looking up at the night sky at sea, it is easier to imagine a great concave surface with the stars and planets moving slowly round. (In reality, of course, it is the Earth that is moving.)

It is convenient to use the idea of a celestial sphere as we can plot the relative positions of the Sun, stars, planets and the Moon at any given time, then transpose those positions to the surface of the Earth and thus find our own position. The essence of finding our position at sea by celestial navigation is the comparison between our dead reckoning position and the observed position of the heavenly body that we are using.

The celestial sphere has its own equator, the **equinoctial**, which lies in the same plane as the Earth's equator. The latitude of a heavenly body, or **declination** on the celestial sphere, is measured north or south from the equinoctial.

In comparison to the celestial sphere, the Earth is minute, so that when observations are made we can imagine that we are at the centre of the Earth. This makes calculations much easier. Positions on the surface of the Earth may also be projected outwards, onto the inner surface of the celestial sphere, so that a vessel's position **A** can be transferred to **X** on the celestial sphere (see Fig 6). Similarly, if the Sun has a declination 15°20′S then this latitude can be transposed to the surface of the Earth. In this

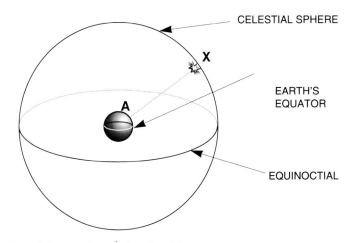

Fig 6 Celestial sphere and equinoctial

way we can, by knowing the position of a heavenly body at any time on the celestial sphere, compare that position to our dead reckoning position on Earth.

We can also project the Greenwich Meridian onto the celestial sphere. At a point when the path of the Sun crosses the equinoctial (celestial equator), when the declination is zero, the east and west factor of a heavenly body can be plotted. This point is called the **First Point of Aries**, and from this point the **Greenwich Hour Angle** (celestial longitude) of any heavenly body is measured westwards.

Figure 7 shows the apparent path of the Sun round the celestial sphere. The Sun reaches a maximum declination of $23\frac{1}{2}°$ north on or about 21 June. It then starts moving south again until it crosses the equinoctial, the **First Point of Libra,** and proceeds to its maximum southerly declination of $23\frac{1}{2}°$ south, then returning northwards to cross the equinoctial again at the First Point of Aries. The path of the Sun round the celestial sphere is called the **ecliptic**, and the angle the Sun makes to the vertical axis is called the obliquity of the ecliptic.

Just as the Sun has an apparent movement around the celestial sphere, so do all the other heavenly bodies. In reality, of course, it is the rotation of the Earth which is causing this effect. However, it is easier to imagine that it is the Sun, stars, planets

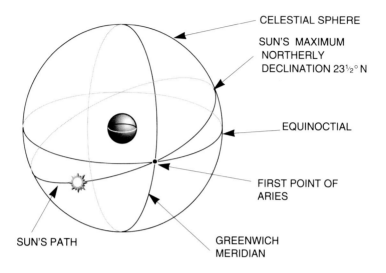

Fig 7 Celestial sphere and Sun's declination

and moons that are rising and setting and also changing their declinations.

The stars do not change their declinations very much and only appear to have a rising and setting motion in the skies. For example, Sirius, a very bright star, only varies its declination by 0.2 or 0.3min away from 16°42′S so that only a rising and setting motion is observed.

In contrast, the Moon moves rapidly about the celestial sphere, changing its declination in one month from 24°S to 27°N. It is this rapid movement of the Moon which calls for strict accuracy when it is being used for navigation.

A last important term that must be understood is **Right Ascension** which is the angular distance eastwards from the First Point of Aries to the meridian of the heavenly body which goes through the Pole and the heavenly body and cuts the equinoctial. The right ascension is always expressed in hours and minutes, from 0000 to 2400 hours.

4
THE PZX TRIANGLE

In celestial navigation it is necessary to be able to solve a spherical triangle, which involves the use of spherical trigonometry. To use this book, however, there is no need to learn the mathematics behind spherical trigonometry. It is sufficient to know that you can solve the PZX triangle by consulting the correct tables: *Nories', Burton's* or *Reed's*.

The PZX triangle on the celestial sphere represents angular measurement along its three sides.

P is the **celestial North Pole**

Z is the point on the celestial sphere directly above the observer and is called the **zenith**

X is the **heavenly body** observed on the celestial sphere.

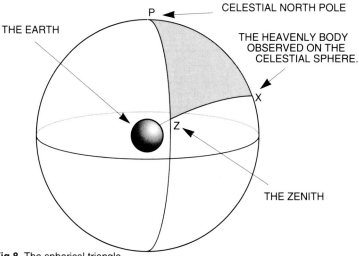

Fig 8 The spherical triangle

In celestial navigation we need to find the value of ZX in the diagram. ZX is the **zenith distance**, an angular measurement of the distance of the body from the observer's zenith.

We can find the value of ZX by using spherical trigonometry and solving the PZX triangle. We can also find ZX by using the sextant, by taking the altitude of the body above the horizon and subtracting that from 90°. This will be explained more fully later. However, it is the comparison between the calculated zenith distance and the observed zenith that tells us where we are.

The PZX Triangle

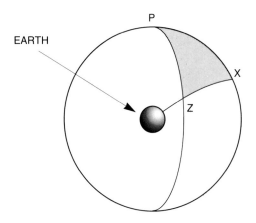

Fig 9 The PZX triangle

The PZX triangle respresents the following:

PX is called the **polar distance** and is, in fact, 90° minus the declination of the body observed.

PZ is called the **arc of the meridian** between the pole and the observer's zenith. This is 90° minus the observer's latitude.

ZX is called the zenith distance.

Angle P represents the **local hour angle** of the body. The local hour angle is a combination of Greenwich Hour Angle and longitude.

Angle Z represents the bearing or **azimuth** of the body.

To find the vessel's position, we need to find ZX. And so, by using spherical trigonometry, we must solve the PZX triangle. To do this we need to know about a formula called the **Haversine Formula**.

Haversine Formula

It is sufficient to know that it states the following:

haversine ZX = haversine P × cosine latitude × cosine declination + haversine (latitude difference declination)

This is usually written as:

hav ZX = havPcos lat cos dec + hav (lat ± dec)

Haversine Tables

Haversine tables can be found in *Nories'* or *Burton's* nautical tables; versines can be found in *Reed's* nautical almanac. You can use either: the result will be the same. *Nories'* and *Burton's* are five-figure tables while *Reed's* are four-figure tables. When using the haversine or versine tables, you have to be careful to use first the log haversine or log versine column, and for the second haversine or versine this has to be taken from the natural haversine or versine column in the tables.

So the formula is:

nat.hav ZX = log havP cos lat cos dec + nat.hav (lat ± dec).

[Note the cosines in the formula are log cosines.]

It will be useful if you make yourself familiar with a particular set of nautical tables, and once you have learned your way around them, then stay with them. It is perfectly possible to sail round the oceans with only a *Reed's*, a sextant and an accurate timepiece. The information given in *Macmillan's* almanac is to be used in conjunction with special calculators. Further mention will be made of this later.

5
THE SEXTANT

The sextant is used for measuring the angle of a heavenly body above the observer's horizon. The sextant has an arc graduated in degrees and a micrometer screw which gives minutes and seconds of arc. There are also telescopes to pinpoint the heavenly body and shades to prevent damage to the eye when using the sun.

There are two mirrors: the **index mirror** and the **horizon mirror**, both of which are used to bring the reflected image of the body down to the horizon when the arm of the sextant is moved.

Types of Sextant

It is not necessary today to pay a lot of money for a sextant, unless you want a traditional one with, perhaps, an expensive telescope for star sights. You can pick up a plastic sextant quite cheaply which will give you adequate accuracy in your positions. The traditional micrometer sextant will give you accuracy, with experience, of a position to about one mile. However, you do need to have practised a lot to achieve this accuracy.

The traditional sextant is much heavier than the plastic sextant. You may therefore find it easier to hold steady in a strong wind or if there is any sea at all.

The best advice is to start with a plastic sextant and see if you can get reliable results. If you can, then you may wish to graduate to the traditional type of sextant, which will inevitably give you more accurate fixes. However, many ocean passages have been made using the simpler, and much cheaper, plastic variety.

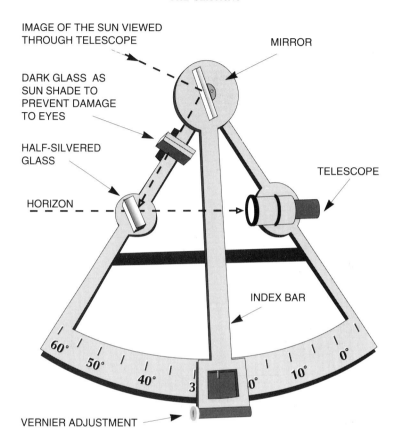

IMAGE OF THE SUN VIEWED
THROUGH TELESCOPE

MIRROR

DARK GLASS AS
SUN SHADE TO
PREVENT DAMAGE
TO EYES

HALF-SILVERED
GLASS

TELESCOPE

HORIZON

INDEX BAR

60°
50°
40°
3
0°
10°
0°

VERNIER ADJUSTMENT

Fig 10 Simplified sextant

Care and Maintenance

The sextant must be treated with great care as it is an exact scientific instrument. The mirrors are at right angles to the frame of the instrument and care must be taken to see that they are not damaged. The sextant should be kept clean and dry and stowed in a safe place in the yacht. When it is being used, make sure that it is resting on its three legs when you put it down.

The sextant should come in its own box, and it should always be stowed in this box when not in use. The arc and the micrometer screw can be kept lightly oiled to prevent corrosion and to help with easy use.

It is advisable to have the sextant checked from time to time by a nautical instrument maker, to make sure that there has been no damage and that it is reading correctly.

Errors of the Sextant

The sextant is a complex instrument to make and assemble. As a result certain errors can be accidentally built in. These are sometimes shown on the lid of the box, and are usually shown on the maker's certificate. The sextant has the following errors:

> *Index error*
> *Side error*
> *Error of perpendicularity*
> *Collimation error*
> *Graduation error*
> *Centring error*
> *Shade error*

These last three errors - Graduation error, Centring error and Shade error - are non-adjustable and should be totalled up on manufacture and shown on the certificate if there is any need for correction to an altitude reading. The first four errors are adjustable.

Manual Adjustments for Errors

Error of Perpendicularity The *first* adjustment should be to correct this error. The index mirror must be at right angles to the plane of the instrument. To check that it is, put the index bar to the centre of the instrument, about sixty degrees. Hold the sextant horizontally, face up and with the arc away from you. Look into the index mirror and see if the true arc and the reflected arcs are in one straight line. If not, the adjustment can be made by turning the small screw at the back of the index mirror until both arcs appear to be in line.

Side Error The *second* adjustment which can be made is to correct side error. This is caused by the horizon mirror not being at right angles to the plane of the instrument. Side error can best be found by using a low-lying star. Hold the sextant vertically, clamp the index bar on zero and put the micrometer screw on zero. Look directly at the star through the telescope and see if the true and reflected star coincide exactly. If they do, then there is no side error. However, if the reflected image appears to lie to one side of the true star, then side error exists. To correct for this, turn the screw at the back of the horizon glass (not the screw nearest the plane of the sextant) to bring the stars coincident with each other.

Index Error The *third* adjustment is for index error, usually found in examination questions abbreviated to I.E. It is expressed as a plus quantity or a minus quantity depending on the error found. Index error is the result of the index glass not being parallel to the horizon glass when the index bar and micrometer screw are set to zero.

The easiest way to check for index error is to use the horizon. If the true and reflected horizons lie in a straight line when holding the sextant vertically, then there is no index error. If the true horizon lies slightly above or below the reflected horizon, then the amount of index error can be found by turning the micrometer screw to bring the two horizons in line with each other. This amount can be read off the micrometer screw, and can be on the positive side of the arc or on the negative side of the arc. It can also be described as being on or off the arc. The stars or the sun can be used in the same way to find this error.

It is possible to correct for index error by adjusting the screw at the back of the horizon glass which is nearest the plane of the instrument. However it is wise not to loosen these screws, and a better course of action may be to allow for the index error found and apply the error to the observed altitudes.

Error of Collimation The *fourth* adjustment is for the error caused by the line of the telescope not being parallel to the plane of the sextant. This error seldom has to be corrected as it is rarely found in modern sextants. If you possess an older sextant, however, the error can be found by placing the two cross wires in the inverting telescope parallel to the plane of the sextant.

Use a low-lying star and place the index bar three or four

degrees either side of zero so that two images of the star can be seen, one at the top and one at the bottom of your field of view. By revolving the eye piece in the telescope, bring the vertical edge of the wires into contact with the top image. If the two images of the star appear in contact with the same edge of the wires, then there is no error. If the two images appear apart, then adjust the screws on the collar of the telescope to bring the two images in line. Some sextants are not fitted with the screws in the collar of the telescope. In this case, the adjustments cannot be made.

Nautical Instrument Makers

If in doubt about how to manually correct for these errors try and find a good nautical instrument maker to check the instrument for you. You should be able to contact a reputable agent through one of the major yacht chandlers. However please note that you will be expected to understand how to apply index error in the RYA examinations as this is the easiest error to find and apply to your sights.

6

THE CHRONOMETER OR
DECK WATCH

Celestial navigation requires accurate time. This can be achieved by having a chronometer, or deck watch, on board your vessel. It is necessary for this timepiece to be accurate to the nearest second of correct time.

A chronometer is always carried on ocean-going vessels so that the correct time can always be known. Indeed, it used to be common practice to have two, so that one could be used if the other became unreliable. The chronometers were checked daily with a time signal from Greenwich to ascertain whether they were running fast or slow when compared with correct time and, if so, by how much. The variation was then recorded on a sheet next to the chronometer. As long as the chronometer was gaining or losing a regular amount each day it did not matter, as the correction in time could be applied to the time on the chronometer.

Now watches are very accurate and maintain their accuracy far more simply than chronometers used to do. An ocean navigator may therefore be tempted to use his or her own watch. It may, however, be prudent to carry a second watch or chronometer which can be kept on Greenwich Mean Time, and can be checked regularly with a time signal to make sure that it is keeping the correct time.

Taking Sights

The chronometer is used every time a sight is taken and needs, as already mentioned, to be accurate with GMT to the nearest second. It is a good idea to get into the habit of reading the watch or chronometer accurately, as mistakes can easily be made in recording the time. When you are taking a sight, you should write down the time and immediately check it again to make sure that you have got it right. Alternatively, you can ask a member of the crew to make a note of the time when you are taking your sights, shouting clearly 'stop' when you want them to record the time. The accuracy of your position will depend upon the accuracy of your timepiece and the accuracy of recording the time.

Fig 11 The Boxed Chronometer

Greenwich Mean Time and Local Time

It is useful to have one timepiece on board which is kept on Greenwich Mean Time and another to be kept on local ship's time. Your time on the yacht will change when you change your longitude. Obviously, your time will change more quickly if you are sailing east or west rather than north or south.

It is common practice at sea to try and keep noon on the ship, when the Sun is overhead or has reached its maximum elevation for that day, and it really depends on the skipper how accurately this happens. It may be more convenient to put your watch back or forwards a regular amount each day as you progress eastwards or westwards. You do not, of course, change the timepiece you are keeping on GMT.

Fifteen degrees of longitude is equal to one hour of time, so if, for example, you are sailing west and changing your longitude by about three degrees a day, then you would put your watch back twelve minutes each day to keep the sun at its maximum elevation as near noon - ship's time - as possible.

The time you keep on your vessel is ship's time, but for celestial navigation this is always referred to as **Local Time**, so you always have to know the time on the vessel and Greenwich Time.

Longitude and Time

Longitude and time are closely related, and the ocean navigator has to understand the relationship to enable the establishment of a position at sea. In the past it was difficult for navigators in sailing ships to establish their longitude accurately because there was invariably no accurate timepiece on board which would enable them to plot an accurate position. Many sailing vessels came to grief on the Australian and American coasts because they were unable accurately to ascertain their longitude or their time.

With the advent of accurate chronometers the present day navigator is able to establish an accurate longitude to within about one or two miles. Even with little experience, accuracy should be obtained to within about five miles. But this in turn depends upon being able to establish the exact time.

As the navigator sails west, the ship's clock should be put back, and on reaching longitude 15°W, ship's time should be one hour *behind* Greenwich Time. This, of course, is due to the rotation of the Earth, but it is still convenient to use the apparent motion of the Sun: rising and setting and reaching a maximum altitude at midday. So, when the vessel is at 15°W, the Sun will be at its maximum elevation one hour *later* than at Greenwich. When sailing eastwards, the reverse is true: at 15°E, ship's time will be one hour *ahead* of Greenwich time.

Perhaps the following little rhyme will help reduce the confusion often caused by the concept of longitude and time:

> *Longitude west, Greenwich time best*
> *Longitude east, Greenwich time least*

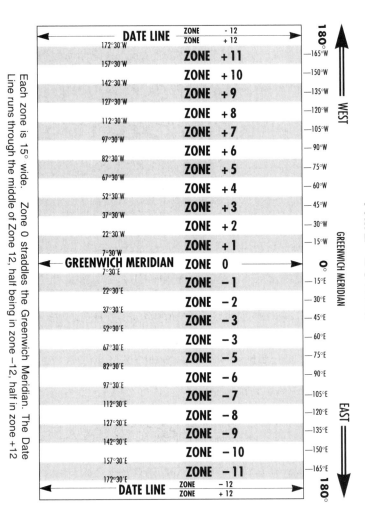

TIME ZONES

Each zone is 15° wide. Zone 0 straddles the Greenwich Meridian. The Date Line runs through the middle of Zone 12, half being in zone –12, half in zone +12

| DATE LINE | ZONE | – 12 |
| | ZONE | + 12 |

172°30′W	
ZONE	+11
157°30′W	
ZONE	+10
142°30′W	
ZONE	+9
127°30′W	
ZONE	+8
112°30′W	
ZONE	+7
97°30′W	
ZONE	+6
82°30′W	
ZONE	+5
67°30′W	
ZONE	+4
52°30′W	
ZONE	+3
37°30′W	
ZONE	+2
22°30′W	
ZONE	+1
7°30′W	
GREENWICH MERIDIAN	ZONE 0
7°30′E	
ZONE	–1
22°30′E	
ZONE	–2
37°30′E	
ZONE	–3
52°30′E	
ZONE	–3
67°30′E	
ZONE	–5
82°30′E	
ZONE	–6
97°30′E	
ZONE	–7
112°30′E	
ZONE	–8
127°30′E	
ZONE	–9
142°30′E	
ZONE	–10
157°30′E	
ZONE	–11
172°30′E	
DATE LINE	ZONE	– 12
	ZONE	+ 12

180° — 165°W — 150°W — 135°W — 120°W — 105°W — 90°W — 75°W — 60°W — 45°W — 30°W — 15°W (WEST)

GREENWICH MERIDIAN 0° — 15°E — 30°E — 45°E — 60°E — 75°E — 90°E — 105°E — 120°E — 135°E — 150°E — 165°E — 180° (EAST)

Fig 12 Time zones

To recap: If you are in westerly longitudes, Greenwich time will be ahead of you; if you are in easterly longitudes, the Sun will rise with you before it does at Greenwich.

Time Zones

For convenience the world is divided into time zones, which are numbered (plus or minus) outwards from the Greenwich Meridian: for every fifteen degrees east of Greenwich, the time will be an additional hour ahead of Greenwich Mean Time; for every fifteen degrees west, the time will be a further hour behind GMT (see Fig 12). The zones are organised so that the *centre* of a zone is always an exact number of hours ahead of or behind Greenwich.

It is convenient, when at sea, to keep ship's time in line with the time zone in which the vessel is positioned. It is impossible to keep the vessel's time on the meridian because as you sail east or west the meridian is always changing.

There are twenty-four time zones: twelve to the west and twelve to the east of Greenwich, meeting at the 180th meridian, better known as the **date line**.

Converting Zone Time to Greenwich Mean Time

Greenwich Mean Time is zone 0, so in zone − 4 the time is four hours ahead of Greenwich, while if you are in zone +5 the time will be five hours behind Greenwich Mean Time. It can be seen from the diagram that whatever longitude you happen to be in, you will be in a time zone. Most countries keep their local time within the time zone, but sometimes **summer time** is kept, which will mean that **local time** will differ from the the zone time.

It is a good idea to keep one deck watch on GMT and, when the vessel crosses into a different time zone, to alter the ship's clock accordingly. As you travel eastwards you will be putting your ship's clock forward, while if you are travelling westwards you will be putting it back. Notice that you will enter time zone Z+1 when you reach longitude 7° 30′ W.

Examples of Converting Time

1. On 2 June in longitude 32° W, ship's time is 1030. What is GMT?

It is necessary to convert arc into time. 32° W is 2 hours and 8 minutes so GMT will be 2hr 8min ahead of ship's time:

Local ship's time	10 30
Longitude	2 08
GMT	12 38

2. Zone time in Z–6 on 10 June is 1545. What is GMT?
Z–6 is six hours ahead of Greenwich. GMT is therefore:

Zone time	15 45
	– 6 00
GMT	09 45

7

FINDING LATITUDE

Y ou will be pleased to know that in celestial navigation finding
latitude is simple compared to finding longitude. Anywhere in
the world, the Sun will reach its maximum altitude during the day
and, if the observer is watching the altitude carefully with the
sextant, the vessel's latitude can easily be found. Nearly two thousand years ago early sailors found latitude very easily using the sim-
plest of sextants. In more recent times, sailing vessels used to sail
along a parallel of latitude. In the text books it was referred to as
'parallel sailing'.

Even with the advent of modern technology, the procedure for
finding latitude at sea using a sextant has barely changed. Satnav
will, of course, give it to you very readily, but the ocean navigator
can still find his latitude each day by using the Sun when it reaches
its maximum altitude - around midday ship's time.

Finding latitude by using the Sun is called *taking a meridian
altitude* as the Sun is said to be on the meridian. In fact, when it is
on your meridian, at midday, it will be bearing due north or south
of you, depending on the time of year and your own dead reckoned
latitude. The meridian is a great circle which goes through the celestial poles and the Earth's poles (see Fig 12).

If you know at what time the Sun should be overhead on your
meridian on a certain day, then, with your sextant, you can watch
for the maximum altitude for about five or ten minutes before that
time. Because the length of the Sun's day varies by as much as
fifteen minutes from one day to the next, this variation has to be
allowed for. The amount of daily variation can be found in the nautical almanacs, under the heading **Time of Meridian Passage**. The
variation is given as a number of minutes before or after noon, and
is often also given as an actual time, such as 1155, indicating that

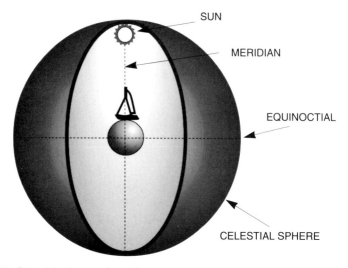

Fig 13 Celestial sphere and meridian

the Sun will be on the meridian five minutes earlier than expected. The Sun reaches its maximum altitude during the day, when it is bearing either due north or due south. If you are $23\frac{1}{2}°$ north, then the Sun's bearing at midday will always be due south, but if you sail further south than this, then at some time the Sun will be bearing north of you. It can be difficult to get an accurate latitude when the Sun's altitude at noon is nearly ninety degrees, as then you cannot be sure whether the Sun reaches its maximum altitude to

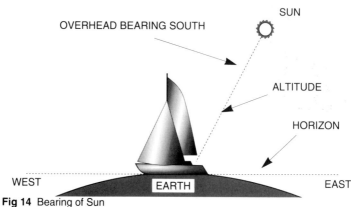

Fig 14 Bearing of Sun

the south or to the north of you. You will find it very difficult to bring the Sun down to the horizon and that it appears to be following you around.

Figure 15 shows the practical aspects of taking a Sun sight at noon. Forgetting the celestial sphere and the mathematics for a moment, you can see that you are measuring the angle of the Sun at noon, reading off the altitude on your sextant by bringing the reflected Sun down to the horizon.

Times of Meridian Passage

As previously stated, the time when the Sun is on the meridian varies from day to day. In the table shown below (which is reproduced from *Reed's Nautical Almanac*), the time of Meridian Passage is shown as **Time of Transit**. The column headed 'Transit' indicates

						⊙		**SUN**		☾
DATE			**Equation of Time**					**Lat. 52°N.**		
Day of					Transit	Semi-diam.	Twi-light	Sun-rise	Sun-set	Twi-light
Yr.	Mth.	Week	0 h.	12 h.						
			m. s.	m. s.	h. m.	′	h. m.	h. m.	h. m.	h. m.
1	1	Fri.	+03 26	+03 40	12 04	16.3	07 28	08 08	15 59	16 40
2	2	Sat.	+03 54	+04 08	12 04	16.3	07 28	08 08	16 00	16 41
3	3	Sun.	+04 22	+04 35	12 05	16.3	07 27	08 08	16 02	16 42
4	4	Mon.	+04 49	+05 03	12 05	16.3	07 27	08 08	16 03	16 43
5	5	Tu.	+05 16	+05 29	12 05	16.3	07 27	08 07	16 04	16 44
6	6	Wed.	+05 43	+05 56	12 06	16.3	07 27	08 07	16 05	16 45
7	7	Th.	+06 09	+06 22	12 06	16.3	07 26	08 07	16 07	16 47
8	8	Fri.	+06 34	+06 47	12 07	16.3	07 26	08 06	16 08	16 48
9	9	Sat.	+07 00	+07 12	12 07	16.3	07 26	08 05	16 09	16 49
10	10	Sun.	+07 24	+07 36	12 08	16.3	07 25	08 05	16 11	16 50
11	11	Mon.	+07 48	+08 00	12 08	16.3	07 25	08 04	16 12	16 52
12	12	Tu.	+08 12	+08 23	12 08	16.3	07 24	08 04	16 14	16 53
13	13	Wed.	+08 35	+08 46	12 09	16.3	07 24	08 03	16 15	16 54
14	14	Th.	+08 57	+09 08	12 09	16.3	07 23	08 02	16 17	16 56
15	15	Fri.	+09 18	+09 29	12 09	16.3	07 22	08 01	16 18	16 57
16	16	Sat.	+09 39	+09 50	12 10	16.3	07 21	08 00	16 20	16 59
17	17	Sun.	+10 00	+10 10	12 10	16.3	07 21	07 59	16 21	17 00
18	18	Mon.	+10 19	+10 29	12 10	16.3	07 20	07 58	16 23	17 02
19	19	Tu.	+10 38	+10 48	12 11	16.3	07 19	07 57	16 25	17 03
20	20	Wed.	+10 57	+11 05	12 11	16.3	07 18	07 56	16 26	17 05
21	21	Th.	+11 14	+11 23	12 11	16.3	07 17	07 55	16 28	17 06
22	22	Fri.	+11 31	+11 39	12 12	16.3	07 16	07 54	16 30	17 08
23	23	Sat.	+11 47	+11 54	12 12	16.3	07 15	07 53	16 32	17 10
24	24	Sun.	+12 02	+12 09	12 12	16.3	07 14	07 51	16 33	17 11
25	25	Mon.	+12 16	+12 23	12 12	16.3	07 13	07 50	16 35	17 13
26	26	Tu.	+12 30	+12 36	12 13	16.3	07 11	07 49	16 37	17 14
27	27	Wed.	+12 43	+12 49	12 13	16.3	07 10	07 47	16 39	17 16
28	28	Th.	+12 55	+13 00	12 13	16.3	07 09	07 46	16 41	17 18
29	29	Fri.	+13 06	+13 11	12 13	16.3	07 08	07 45	16 42	17 19
30	30	Sat.	+13 16	+13 21	12 13	16.3	07 06	07 43	16 44	17 21
31	31	Sun.	+13 25	+13 30	12 13	16.3	07 05	07 42	16 46	17 23

Fig 15 Transit table from *Reed's*

37

how many minutes after noon the Sun will be on the meridian, ie overhead bearing south or north on your meridian of longitude. This table is shown for each month of the year, so you will be able to trace the variations of the Sun's transit time.

It is important to know as accurately as possible when the Sun is going to reach its maximum altitude each day. For this, you must know your longitude and be able to convert it into time. For example, if the longitude of your vessel at noon is going to be 15°W, then you know that the Sun will be overhead one hour later than at Greenwich. So, if your ship's time is one hour later than Greenwich, then the Sun should be overhead at 1200. Using the correction from the Transit table for, say, the 14th, you can see that the Sun will be overhead on your meridian at 1209. Greenwich time will be 1309.

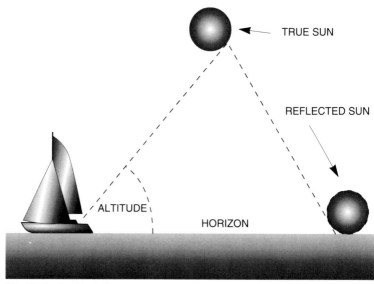

Fig 16 Sun's altitude by sextant

By rocking the sextant (see page 15, Fig 5) you will be able to make the lower limb of the Sun just kiss the horizon and it is this accuracy which will give you an altitude reading and hence your latitude. There are corrections to be made to this altitude. We should really be using the centre of the Sun and the centre of the Earth and taking the observation from sea level. Therefore, the following corrections have to be made:

Dip is the term used for the amount of error when not at sea level, and in the tables the observer's height of eye, in feet or metres above sea level, is taken into account (see Fig 17).

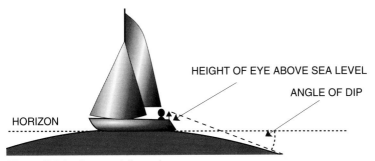

Fig 17 Height of eye and dip angle

Semi-diameter is the term used for not using the centre of the Sun. The value of the Sun's semi-diameter has to be taken into account, and this value is found in the monthly tables. The value does not vary very much; it is around sixteen minutes of arc. (The diameter of the Sun is about thirty-two minutes of arc.)

Horizontal Parallax is the term used for the correction that has to be made for not using the centre of the Earth, for using its surface instead. A set of tables called the *Sun's Altitude Total Correction Tables* gives the necessary corrections and can be found in the nautical almanacs. An example is set out at the end of this section. The table is easy to use and the amount can be applied directly to the sextant altitude. The criteria used for the table are the **height of eye** of the observer and the **observed altitude** on the sextant. A small monthly correction must also be applied. This is shown at the foot of the table. The correction for the Sun is always additive, if the lower limb of the Sun is used. The figures for observed altitude at the head of the table are shown in metres (top) and feet (below). In *Macmillan's* almanac, the Dip tables are shown separately, and the reading has to be applied to the observed altitude of the sun. Observations of the true altitude of the Sun and other heavenly bodies can be affected by refraction of light, which has the effect of 'bending' the angles. To minimise the effects of refraction, the Sun should not be observed for a sight which gives a sextant angle of less than 20° above the horizon.

Time of Meridian Passage

As part of the RYA Ocean syllabus you will be asked to find out the time of meridian passage. Below is a worked example and some for you to try yourself:

Worked Example

Dead Reckon. longitude at noon	25°	35′ W	
Converted into times gives	1hr	42min	20sec
Greenwich time at noon	12	00	00
Greenwich time of sun overhead			
at that longitude	13	42	20
Correction for date (30th)	+ 13	00	
Corrected time	13	55	20 GMT

So, if you are keeping time by Greenwich, then you will be looking for the Sun to be on your meridian at about 1355 GMT; if you are keeping ship's time and, because of your longitude, have your clock set two hours different to Greenwich, then the Sun will be on the meridian at about 1155.

Sample Questions

1 Find the GMT of meridian passage on the 8th in longitude 51° 26′ W.

2 Find the GMT of meridian passage on the 28th in longitude 10° 18′ E.

3 Find the GMT of meridian passage on the 12th in longitude 112° 48′ W.

4 Find the GMT of meridian passage on the 2nd in longitude 156° 29′ E.

Having found the time the Sun is going to reach its maximum altitude for the day, ie on the meridian, we need to find that altitude. We do this by using the sextant. By rocking the sextant so that the lower limb of the Sun is touching the horizon we can watch and see when the maximum altitude is reached. This is not as difficult as it sounds. It will be quite clear when the sun stops rising and you will then be able to stop winding the micrometer to bring the Sun down onto the horizon and take a reading on the vernier scale.

Some more examples :

1 A vessel is in DR position 25° 30′ N, 35° 15′ W, at noon on 20 May. Height of eye is 3 metres; index error is 2′.0 on the arc. Find the observed latitude at noon if the Sun's altitude was 84° 20′ and the declination was 20° 01′ N.

Observed altitude	84°	20′.0
Index error		− 2′.0
	84°	18′.0
Total correction		+ 12′.7
	84°	30′.7
	90°	00′
	5°	29′.3
Add Sun's declination	20°	00′.3 N
Observed noon latitude	25°	29′.6 N

[Interpolate declination for 1430:

For 1400	20°	00′.1 N
For 1600	20°	01′.1 N
For 1430	20°	00′.3 N]

It is reassuring to have confirmation that your DR position is fairly accurate. In this example the Sun is bearing south at noon. If the vessel had a DR position of 14° 30′ N, 35° 15′ W, then the Sun would be bearing north at noon and the 5° 29′.3 would be subtracted from the declination to give a latitude of 14° 31′ N.

For example:

Observed altitude	84°	20′.0
Index Error		− 2′.0
	84°	18′.0
		+ 12′.7
	84°	30′.7
	90°	00′.0
	− 5°	29′.3
	20°	00′.3 N
Observed noon latitude	14°	31′.0 N

It may be useful to remember a simple rule for adding or subtracting the complement of the altitude to the declination:

SAME names ADD, DIFFERENT names SUBTRACT

But to do this you always have to reverse the bearing of the Sun. So, in the above example, the 5° 29′.3 would be ascribed south if the Sun was bearing north. This may seem confusing, and may best be ignored if you can think out whether you should add or subtract.

Sun's Declination

When trying to find a vessel's latitude, the Sun's celestial latitude, or declination, must be used. If we refer back to the celestial sphere, we are using the declination of the Sun on the celestial sphere to relate to our own earthly latitude. If on 21 June our DR latitude at noon was 23°30′, then we would have the same celestial latitude as the Sun and on our sextant the Sun would be vertically above us at 90°. If we followed the Sun we would have to keep the Sun at 90° overhead at noon every day, so in reality a noon meridian altitude is giving us the angular distance we are from the Sun's own latitude, or declination. To arrive at our own latitude on Earth, we have to apply the Sun's declination to our observed altitude of the Sun, taken away from 90° as we are measuring the angle from the poles and not the equator.

It is difficult to show diagrammatically what happens, but in Fig 18 the line AB represents the earthly horizon. The Sun has moved along its celestial path until it reaches its declination of 23°. The observer's altitude of the Sun is 63°. The angle of the observer's Sun from the observer's zenith is 27°. If, therefore, you combine the Sun's declination of 23° with 27°, you can see that the observer on earth has a latitude of 50°. This would be the situation in June in the northern hemisphere.

Let us suppose it is February, the Sun has a southerly declination, and we are in our same latitude of 25°30′ N (see Fig 19). The Sun has a declination of about eleven degrees in February, so we would expect the Sun at noon to have an altitude of about fifty-four degrees. Find the latitude at noon if the DR position of the vessel is 25°30′ N, 35°15′ W. Height of eye is 3 metres, index error 2.0′ on the arc, if the Sun's altitude was 53°20′ and its declination on

February 20 was 10° 54′ S.
Here is the worked example:

Observed altitude	53°	20′.0
Index error		− 2′.0
	53°	18′.0
Total correction		+ 12′.0
	53°	30′.0
	90°	00′
	36°	30′.0 (N)
Sun's declination	10°	54′.0 S
Observed latitude	25°	36′.0 N

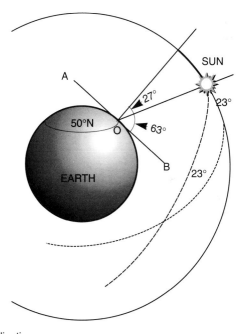

Fig 18 Sun's declination

In this case, the Sun is bearing south at noon, reverse bearing to north, so we have different names, so we must subtract the declination from 36° 30′.

In the diagram (Fig 19):

$H\text{-}H_1$ represents the observer's horizon
EQ   represents the equinoctial
Z   represents the observer's zenith
S_1 represents the Sun on the ecliptic at 11°S of the equinoctial
S_2 represents the Sun on the celestial sphere
A   represents the Sun's altitude from the observer

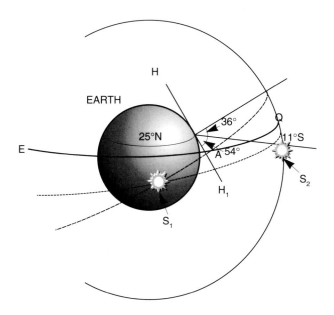

Fig 19 Finding latitude

Here are some examples of finding latitude when the sun will be on the meridian:

Example 1 (Use the tables found in the Appendix)
A vessel is in DR position 42° 15′ N, 22° 45′ W, at noon on 10 June. Find the time the sun will be on the meridian and also the observed latitude at noon. Height of eye is 12ft, index error is 1′.5 off the arc. Sextant altitude of the Sun is 70° 30′.

To find GMT when the Sun will be on the meridian:

Longitude 22° 45′ W = 1hr 31min 00sec

GMT	12	00	00
Long	1	31	00 W
	13	31	00 GMT the Sun will be on the meridian

The correction for time of transit from the table for 10 June gives 1207, so the GMT of the time the Sun will be on the meridian will be 13hr 38min 00sec. If the time on the ship is one hour behind Greenwich time, then ship's time will be 12 38 00.

To find latitude:

Observed altitude	70°	30′
Index error		+ 1′.5
	70°	31′.5
Total correction		12′.1
	70°	43′.6
	90°	00′.
	19°	16′.4 (N)
Declination	23°	01′.0 N
Latitude	42°	17′.6 N

Example 2

A vessel is in DR position 12° 27′ N, 35° 46′ W, at noon on 23 October. Find the time the Sun will be on the meridian if ship's time is two hours behind Greenwich. Height of eye is 8ft, index error is 2′.0 on the arc. The sextant altitude of the Sun is 66° 02′. (Use the tables found in the Appendix.)

Example 3

A vessel is in the Pacific, approaching Auckland, New Zealand. Its DR position at noon on 2 June is 35° 20′ S, 176° 43′ W. Find the GMT at which the Sun will be on the meridian and the observed latitude at noon if the height of eye is 6ft and the index error is 2′.3 on the arc. The sextant altitude of the sun is 32° 18′.

Ex-meridian Latitude

Even if it is cloudy and the Sun is obscured, it is still possible to

SUN ALTITUDE TOTAL CORRECTION TABLE
For correcting the Observed Altitude of the Sun's Lower Limb

ALWAYS ADDITIVE (+)
Height of the eye above the sea. Top line metres, lower line feet

Obs. Alt.	0.9	1.8	2.4	3	3.7	4.3	4.9	5.5	6	7.6	9	12	15	18	21	24
	3	6	8	10	12	14	16	18	20	25	30	40	50	60	70	80
9	8.6	8.0	7.6	7.2	6.9	6.6	6.4	6.2	5.9	5.4	4.9	4.1	3.4	2.7	2.1	1.5
10	9.1	8.5	8.1	7.9	7.5	7.2	7.0	6.7	6.6	6.0	5.5	4.7	3.9	3.3	2.7	2.1
11	9.6	9.0	8.6	8.3	8.0	7.7	7.4	7.2	7.0	6.4	6.0	5.2	4.4	3.7	3.1	2.5
12	10.0	9.4	9.0	8.7	8.4	8.1	7.8	7.6	7.4	6.8	6.4	5.6	4.8	4.1	3.5	2.9
13	10.3	9.7	9.3	9.0	8.7	8.4	8.2	7.9	7.7	7.2	6.7	5.9	5.2	4.5	3.9	3.3
14	10.6	10.0	9.6	9.3	9.0	8.7	8.5	8.2	8.0	7.5	7.0	6.2	5.5	4.8	4.2	3.6
15	10.9	10.2	9.9	9.5	9.2	9.0	8.7	8.5	8.2	7.7	7.2	6.4	5.7	5.0	4.4	3.8
16	11.1	10.5	10.1	9.7	9.5	9.2	8.9	8.7	8.5	7.9	7.5	6.7	5.9	5.2	4.6	4.1
17	11.3	10.7	10.3	10.0	9.7	9.4	9.1	8.9	8.7	8.2	7.7	6.9	6.1	5.5	4.9	4.3
18	11.5	10.8	10.5	10.1	9.9	9.6	9.3	9.1	8.9	8.3	7.9	7.0	6.3	5.6	5.0	4.5
19	11.6	11.0	10.6	10.3	10.0	9.7	9.5	9.2	9.0	8.5	8.0	7.2	6.5	5.8	5.2	4.6
20	11.8	11.2	10.8	10.4	10.2	9.9	9.6	9.4	9.2	8.6	8.2	7.4	6.6	5.9	5.3	4.8
21	11.9	11.3	10.9	10.6	10.3	10.0	9.8	9.5	9.3	8.8	8.3	7.5	6.8	6.1	5.5	4.9
22	12.0	11.4	11.0	10.7	10.4	10.1	9.9	9.7	9.4	8.9	8.4	7.6	6.9	6.2	5.6	5.0
23	12.1	11.5	11.1	10.8	10.5	10.2	10.0	9.8	9.5	9.0	8.5	7.7	7.0	6.3	5.7	5.1
24	12.2	11.6	11.2	10.9	10.6	10.3	10.1	9.9	9.6	9.1	8.6	7.8	7.1	6.4	5.8	5.2
25	12.3	11.7	11.3	11.0	10.7	10.4	10.2	10.0	9.7	9.2	8.7	7.9	7.2	6.5	5.9	5.3
26	12.4	11.8	11.4	11.1	10.8	10.5	10.3	10.1	9.8	9.3	8.8	8.0	7.3	6.6	6.0	5.4
27	12.5	11.9	11.5	11.2	10.9	10.6	10.4	10.1	9.9	9.4	8.9	8.1	7.4	6.7	6.1	5.5
28	12.6	12.0	11.6	11.3	11.0	10.7	10.4	10.2	10.0	9.5	9.0	8.2	7.4	6.8	6.2	5.6
30	12.7	12.1	11.7	11.4	11.1	10.8	10.6	10.4	10.1	9.6	9.1	8.3	7.6	6.9	6.3	5.7
32	12.9	12.2	11.9	11.5	11.2	11.0	10.7	10.5	10.2	9.7	9.3	8.4	7.7	7.0	6.4	5.8
34	13.0	12.3	12.0	11.6	11.3	11.1	10.8	10.6	10.3	9.8	9.4	8.5	7.8	7.1	6.5	5.9
36	13.1	12.4	12.1	11.7	11.4	11.2	10.9	10.7	10.4	9.9	9.5	8.6	7.9	7.2	6.6	6.0
38	13.2	12.5	12.1	11.8	11.5	11.2	11.0	10.8	10.5	10.0	9.5	8.7	8.0	7.3	6.7	6.1
40	13.3	12.6	12.2	11.9	11.6	11.3	11.1	10.8	10.6	10.1	9.6	8.8	8.1	7.4	6.8	6.2
42	13.4	12.7	12.3	12.0	11.7	11.4	11.2	10.9	10.7	10.2	9.7	8.9	8.2	7.5	6.9	6.3
44	13.4	12.7	12.4	12.0	11.7	11.5	11.2	11.0	10.7	10.2	9.8	8.9	8.2	7.5	6.9	6.3
46	13.5	12.8	12.4	12.1	11.8	11.5	11.3	11.0	10.8	10.3	9.8	9.0	8.3	7.6	7.0	6.4
48	13.6	12.9	12.5	12.2	11.9	11.6	11.3	11.1	10.9	10.4	9.9	9.1	8.3	7.7	7.1	6.4
50	13.6	12.9	12.5	12.2	11.9	11.6	11.4	11.1	10.9	10.4	9.9	9.1	8.4	7.7	7.1	6.5
52	13.6	13.0	12.6	12.3	12.0	11.7	11.4	11.2	11.0	10.5	10.0	9.2	8.4	7.8	7.2	6.5
54	13.7	13.0	12.6	12.3	12.0	11.7	11.5	11.3	11.0	10.5	10.0	9.2	8.5	7.8	7.2	6.6
56	13.7	13.1	12.7	12.4	12.1	11.8	11.5	11.3	11.1	10.6	10.1	9.3	8.5	7.9	7.3	6.7
58	13.8	13.1	12.7	12.4	12.1	11.8	11.6	11.3	11.1	10.6	10.1	9.3	8.6	7.9	7.3	6.8
60	13.8	13.1	12.8	12.4	12.1	11.9	11.6	11.4	11.1	10.6	10.2	9.3	8.6	7.9	7.3	6.8
62	13.9	13.2	12.8	12.5	12.2	11.9	11.7	11.4	11.2	10.7	10.2	9.4	8.7	8.0	7.4	6.8
64	13.9	13.2	12.8	12.5	12.2	11.9	11.7	11.5	11.2	10.7	10.2	9.4	8.7	8.0	7.4	6.9
66	14.0	13.2	12.9	12.6	12.3	12.0	11.7	11.5	11.3	10.7	10.3	9.5	8.7	8.1	7.5	6.9
70	14.1	13.3	12.9	12.6	12.3	12.0	11.8	11.6	11.3	10.8	10.3	9.5	8.8	8.1	7.5	7.0
80	14.2	13.5	13.1	12.8	12.5	12.2	11.9	11.7	11.5	11.0	10.5	9.7	8.9	8.3	7.7	7.1
90	14.3	13.6	13.2	12.9	12.6	12.3	12.1	11.9	11.6	11.1	10.6	9.8	9.1	8.4	7.8	7.2

MONTHLY CORRECTION

Jan.	Feb.	Mar.	Apr.	May	June	July	Aug.	Sept.	Oct.	Nov.	Dec.
+0'.3	+0'.2	+0'.1	0'.0	−0'.1	−0'.2	−0'.2	−0'.2	−0'.1	+0'.1	+0'.2	+0'.3

Fig 21 Sun Altitude Correction Table from *Reed's*

find the latitude at noon as long as it is within half an hour of the time of meridian passage. In this case it is called an ex-meridian latitude. Let us suppose that the Sun is on the meridian at, say, 1148 but at that moment it becomes obscured by a cloud. However, fifteen minutes later it again becomes visible. If a sight is taken immediately, and the time noted, then latitude can still be found. There are special ex-meridian tables produced by *Nories'* or *Burton's*, but these cannot be found in the almanacs.

Pole Star

If you are in the northern hemisphere, a vessel's latitude can be found at dawn or dusk by using the Pole Star, in conjunction with the special table to be found in the almanacs. Unfortunately, the Pole Star is not very bright and it may prove difficult to bring it down to the horizon except on a clear night with a good horizon. The Pole Star, Polaris, can be found by following the pointers of the constellation stars in the Plough or Great Bear (see Fig 19).
The use of Polaris will be dealt with fully in Chapter 10 which deals with stars and position finding.

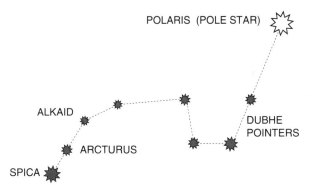

Fig 22 Pole Star

Other Methods of finding Latitude

It is also possible to find latitude by taking an observation of a star or planet when it is on the meridian and bearing either due north or south, or nearly so. This is also possible using the Moon.

47

8

FINDING LONGITUDE

Finding longitude is a more complex process than finding latitude. It depends upon being able to solve the PZX triangle and on obtaining a comparison between the observed zenith distance and the calculated zenith distance. You will remember that this is side ZX in the PZX triangle. Obtaining an accurate longitude position depends on three actions:

1 taking a good sight with your sextant
2 recording the time accurately
3 working up your sight without any mistakes.

Taking a sight

The first skill you need is the ability to take an accurate Sun sight from a small moving boat. You will have to carefully wedge yourself somewhere so that you can 'rock' the sextant to get a good sight. It is probably easier to get a member of your crew to record the time when you take the sight. Shout 'stop' when you wish the time to be recorded. It is wise to take three sights in quick succession and work all three, using the mean figure in your final calculation. As long as the Sun is more than twenty degrees above the horizon (thus avoiding errors creeping in as a consequence of refraction), it is best to take longitude in the morning, at about 0830 ship's time. It should be taken again between 1530 and 1600 as a check on the morning's finding.

In Figure 23, O is the observer on the surface of the Earth and Z is the zenith directly overhead. X is the Sun, which has an angular distance ZX from the zenith. ZX is 90° *minus* your sextant altitude, which is called the **observer's zenith distance**. The observer's position on the surface of the Earth is the DR position. At a certain time

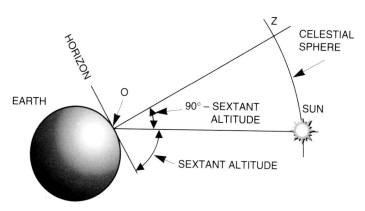

Fig 23 Sextant altitude

it is possible to find the calculated zenith distance by using the information in the nautical almanacs and tables, and thus compare the observed zenith distance with the calculated zenith distance. The difference between the two is called the **intercept**. If the difference between the calculated zenith distance and the observed zenith distance is zero, then it means that your DR position is correct with your observed position, or your DR longitude is correct. The greater the longitude, the more inaccurate the DR longitude will be.

In Figure 24 overleaf, PP_1 represents the Sun's meridian on the celestial sphere. Z is the observer's zenith. HH_1 is the horizon on Earth; O is the observer. So angle XOH_1 represents altitude on the sextant. Angle ZOX is 90°– altitude, which is side ZX.

On the celestial sphere is triangle PZX. PeOPe on Earth is the meridian of the observer, which is the longitude on Earth as PXP_1 represents the meridian of longitude on the celestial sphere. So, by solving the PZX triangle in the celestial sphere and by comparing it with our observed zenith distance from the sextant, we can see if the two longitudes will be the same or if there is a difference.

Different Methods of Obtaining Longitude

Over the years much has changed in finding longitude. In the early nineteenth century it was difficult to find longitude accurately. It wasn't until vessels were able to have an accurate timepiece on

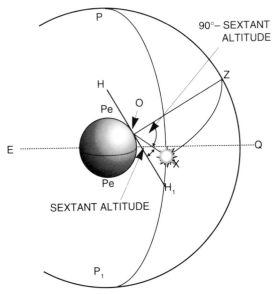

Fig 24 Establishing longtitude

board, and the mathematical formula had been worked out, that longitude could be found to the nearest nautical mile.

In about 1850 a Frenchman called Marq St Hilaire invented a new mathematical formula for solving the PZX triangle. This method of comparing zenith distances is called unsurprisingly the **Marq St Hilaire** method. It has stood the test of time and until only recently was the standard method used with the help of either *Nories'* or *Burton's* tables and a nautical almanac.

With the advent of computers, quicker methods have been found to solve the PZX triangle. Today, the *Sight Reduction for Air Navigation Tables*, which give the equivalent of the calculated zenith distance in a few moments, are used. The electronic calculator has made doing the mathematics involved much easier: the information given in *Macmillan's* almanac is geared to the use of calculators.

Satellite navigation, of course, will accurately pinpoint a vessel's position without any calcuation or sextant work at all as the position is given as a latitude and longitude reading. However it must always be remembered that any complicated piece of electronic equipment can fail and there are not too many service agents in mid-Atlantic.

The following pages are devoted to showing the student how the PZX triangle is solved by the Marq St Hilaire method: firstly, using *Reed's* nautical almanac, which has all the necessary mathematical tables; and secondly, using the air tables in conjunction with the nautical almanac. Note these same methods apply whether you are using the Sun, stars, planets or the Moon.

Marq St Hilaire and Reed's Nautical Almanac

When using any method of solving the PZX triangle, it is easier if the calculation is broken down into areas. To remind you of the information required for solving the triangle the formula is:

Nat/versine ZX = Versine P × log cosine lat × log cosine
declination + natural versine lat difference declination

You need:

P = the local hour angle (LHA)

DR = dead reckoned position with latitude and longitude

Declination of body observed

Local hour angle is found by applying the DR longitude to the GHA at the time of sight.

For example:

A vessel in position 15° 09′ N, 34° 28′ W, takes a sextant altitude of the Sun at 0830 ship's time when the deck watch gave 10hr 45min 20sec on 8 June. Find the local hour angle.

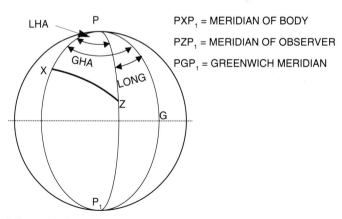

PXP₁ = MERIDIAN OF BODY

PZP₁ = MERIDIAN OF OBSERVER

PGP₁ = GREENWICH MERIDIAN

Fig 25 Different Meridians

GHA for 8 June	330°	15′.8	at 1000
GHA correction	11°	20′.0	for 45min 20sec
	341°	35′.8	
Longitude	34°	28′.0W	
Local Hour Angle	307°	07′.8	

Longitude west, Greenwich time best. We need local time, so longitude is subtracted from the Greenwich Hour Angle.

Example 2 Having found the hour angle, you can now proceed to solve the PZX triangle. We will use the last example, but add a little information. On 8 June a vessel is in DR position 15° 09′ N, 34° 28′ W. At 0830 ship's time a sextant altitude of the Sun gave 39° 31′. The index error was 2′.5 off the arc; the height of eye was 10ft. Deck watch gave 10hr 45min 20sec, which was correct with GMT. Find zenith distance.

GHA for 8 June	330°	15′.8
GHA correction for 45m20s	+11°	20′.0
	341°	35′.8
Longitude west	34°	28′.0
Local Hour Angle (LHA)	307°	07′.8

[Sun's declination for 10 45 = 22° 50′.7 N]

From *Reed's* Versine Table:

Log versine LHA	9.5981
Log cosine latitude	9.9846
Log cosine declination	9.9645
	9.5472

[Latitude	15°	09′.0N
Declination	22°	50′.7N
Lat Diff Declination	7°	41′.7N]

Change this figure to natural versine	0.3525
+ lat difference declination	0.0090
Natural versine ZX	0.3615

ZX   =   50° 19′

[This is the **calculated zenith distance**]

Use of Logs and Tables

A reminder about the use of logs. When you are multiplying log functions, you add them together. The 9. indicates that this is −1, an 8. is −2, a 7. is −3 and so on. In nautical log tables you will always find this. So adding together 9 three times gives 7, or minus three, but in this case we are carrying 20, so you are still left with 9., or −1. The figures are always additive, so you should soon get used to it. Remember that in the *versine* table you will be going from the bottom of the page when you are using larger numbers. The *minute* column also starts from the bottom.

To avoid making mistakes later on, it might be a good idea to practice taking figures out of the versine table. The log versine column is in darker print than the natural versine column.

Using the versine table, try the following:

(a) Find the log versine of 57° 36′
(b) Find the log versine of 305° 47′
(c) Find the natural versine of 21° 36′
(d) Change log. 9.9458 to natural versine
(e) Change log. 8.6940 to natural versine

To return to our worked example, we have found ZX (zenith distance) 50°19′.5. This is the *calculated* zenith distance, which we now have to compare with the *observed* zenith distance we found on the sextant, in order to find the intercept.

Sextant altitude	39°	31′
Index error		+2′.5
	39°	33′.5
Total correction		11′.5
	39°	45′.0
	90°	00′.0
Observed ZX	50°	15′.0
Calculated ZX	50°	19′.0
Intercept		4′.0 E (T)(towards)

The intercept is named towards or away from the body observed, and in this case suggests that you are 4 miles further east than your DR longitude. This is not quite correct, however, because we have not yet considered the bearing, or azimuth, of the Sun. If the Sun was bearing due east, then we would be about 4 miles east of the DR position, but as can be seen in the next diagram (Fig 26), it will

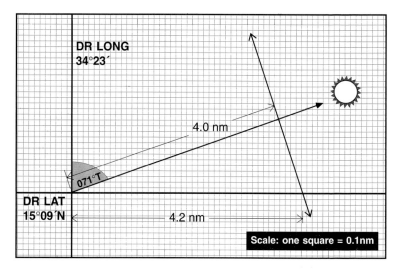

Fig 26 Plot 1

be a little more than 4 miles. First, however, we have to find out what the bearing of the Sun was at the time of taking the sight. To do this, you can use the ABC tables in *Reed's*. The tables are self-explanatory. You will need LHA, latitude and declination.

A = .202 +
B = .505 –
C = .303 = E 19°N or 071°True

In Figure 26 the observer is shown at the DR position. The intercept of 4 nautical miles (drawn to a suitable scale) is shown along the bearing of the Sun, so this, in fact, gives an indication that the vessel is about 4 miles east of the DR longitude.

In reality, this is only true if you are at the equator, where one mile east or west is equal to one minute of longitude. So we have to convert our five miles into minutes of longitude. This can be done quite simply with the aid of the table in *Reed's* almanac entitled

Departure into Dlong and Vice Versa. Departure is the distance in nautical miles measured in an east-west direction. As all meridians of longitude converge at the poles, it can be seen that latitude is the criteria of Dlong. The formula is:

Dlong = *Departure × secant latitude*

In our case therefore:

Dlong = 4.5 × secant 15°
= 4.5 × 1.04 (from table)
= 4.8 minutes of longitude.

So our position at 0830 is 15° 09′ N, 34° 23′ W.

In fact, the vessel is somewhere along the position line PL and it will not be until noon, when we can check our latitude, that we will know whether we are north or south of our DR latitude. However, by doing a running fix, and using this position for a run to noon, we can obtain a noon position.

Position Lines, Intercepts and Azimuths

In celestial navigation the position line is in reality a position circle, but because the distances are so great we can draw the circle as a straight line. The position line is always drawn at right angles to the bearing of the heavenly body.

In Figure 24:

O   is the **observer's position**
ZX   is the **calculated zenith distance**
Z_1X is the **observed zenith distance**
OA   is the **intercept**
AP   is the **position circle**
Z   is the **observer's zenith**
X   is the **heavenly body**

So the intercept is the difference between the calculated zenith distance and the observed zenith distance. It is also a comparison between the observer's DR position and the calculated distance from that DR position.

If the observed zenith distance is greater than the calculated zenith distance, the vessel's position is further away from the DR position and is called **away**. If the observed zenith distance is less than the calculated zenith distance, then the vessel's position is nearer the DR position and is called **towards**. The azimuth is another name for the bearing of the Sun.

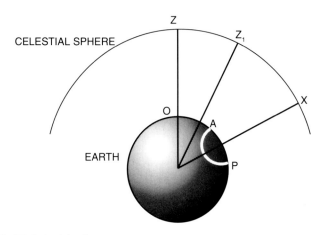

Fig 27 Celestial sphere

In the PZX triangle the azimuth is angle PZX (see Fig 28).

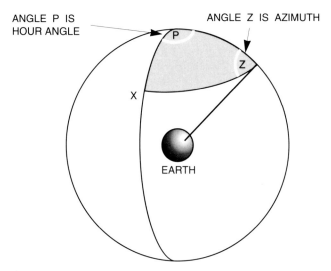

Fig 28 Azimuth

Finding Longitude using Sight Reduction (Air) Tables

For this method, a chosen position, which is close to the vessel's DR position, is used. When finding the local hour angle, the minutes of longitude are rounded up to make a whole degree when adding or subtracting the DR longitude to the Greenwich Hour Angle.

For example:
A vessel is in DR position 39° 08′ N, 25° 16′ W. At 0830 on 5 June an observation was made of the Sun's lower limb. The time zone was +2, the deck watch time was 10hr 12min 07sec and its error was 2min 24sec slow. The sextant altitude was 41° 21′ and the index error was 2′.1 on the arc. If the height of eye was 3 metres, what was the assumed position, intercept and azimuth?

The air tables show LHA, latitude and declination. First find LHA as with the Marq St Hilaire method:

Deck watch time	10hr	12min	07sec
Correction		2min	24sec
GMT	10hr	14min	31sec

GHA for 10 00		330°	24′.0
Correction 14min 31sec		3°	37′.8
		334°	01′.8

Longitude (chosen)		25°	01′.8 W
Local hour angle		309°	00′.0

The chosen longitude is 25° 01′.8 so that the LHA is a whole number of degrees.

The air tables can now be entered with latitude 39° 00′ N and declination 22° 32′ N (latitude and declination same name).

Columns of figures given are:

Hc   this is the calculated altitude (not zenith distance)

d   this is the correction to be made to Hc for the minutes of declination

There is a special table (Table 5) which is used to correct the tabulated altitude for minutes of declination. This is reproduced at the back of this book. Look down the column with declination 22° as far as LHA 309° and read off:

Hc =   43°   34'
d   =   +33'
Z   =   96

Go to the declination correction table and read off 33' and 32' (minutes of declination) and find 18'.

Add this 18' to the tabulated altitude:

$$\begin{array}{ll} 43° & 34' \\ + & 18' \\ \hline 43° & 52' \end{array}$$

You now have a revised tabulated altitude of 43° 52'.

The azimuth, or bearing of the Sun, is 096° T.

Look carefully at the small print at the top and bottom of the page to establish the correct bearing. The bearing depends upon the value of the LHA.

Having found the tabulated altitude, you now need to compare this with the corrected sextant altitude to find the intercept, thus:

Sextant altitude	43°	21'
Index error		– 2'.1
	43°	18'.9
Total correction		11'.8
Observed altitude	43°	30'.7
Tabulated altitude	43°	52'.0
Intercept		21'.3(A)

As we have seen, the intercept is named *towards* the body if the observed altitude is greater than the tabulated altitude; it is named *away* from the body if the observed altitude is less than the tabulated altitude.

To find the assumed position you must now plot this information on to squared paper or on the chart (Fig 26). The bearing of 096° is laid off from 25° 01'.8 W and the intercept is measured off 21.3miles from that point **A** away from the Sun. This gives a distance of 23.5miles westwards from 25° W, which has to be converted into minutes of longitude by the formula:

Dlong = departure × secant latitude

Dlong = 23.5 × 1.29

≈ 30' of Dlong

So our new assumed position is 39° 00' N, 25° 30' W

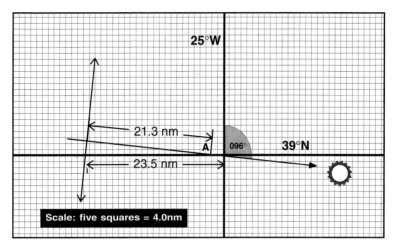

25°W

21.3 nm

A 096° **39°N**

23.5 nm

Scale: five squares = 4.0nm

Fig 29 Plot 2

When using this method, the intercepts are likely to be larger as you are using a *chosen* longitude instead of your **DR** longitude. The latitude remains at 39° 00′ N as that is what you have used from the tables, and will only be corrected when you are able to obtain a meridian altitude or star sight. Remember so far we have obtained only our longtitude. This has to be crossed with our latitude in order to fix our position.

9

POSITION FIXING USING
THE SUN-RUN METHOD

The principle behind this method is the same as that behind taking a running fix to plot your position on the chart when you can only take bearings of one object. In a similar way, in celestial navigation, you can use the Sun as one object and take two sights at different times with the run of the vessel in between the sights, and transfer the position lines found to gain a position.

It is usual practice at sea to obtain a morning sight which will give a longitude, and using the course and speed of the vessel to run this sight to noon, when a latitude is obtained. By crossing the two position lines obtained, a noon position can be found. The latitude at noon is only a horizontal position line which lies at right angles to the due north or south bearing of the Sun.

For example

On 14 June a vessel was in DR position 10° 20′ S, 132° 55′ W, aproaching the Marquesas Islands in the Pacific. At 0815 ship's time an observed altitude of the Sun with a sextant read 25° 11′. Index error was 1′.5 on the arc, height of eye was 8ft. The deck watch time was 17hr 05min 22sec, which was correct with GMT. Between 0815 and noon the vessel sailed a course of 295°(T) for a distance of 20 miles. At noon a sextant meridian altitude of the Sun gave 56° 25′. Find the vessel's position at noon.

1 To find Local Hour Angle (LHA)

GHA for 1600	59°	57′.0
Correction for 1hr	15°	00′.0
Correction for 5min22sec	1°	20′.5
Corrected GHA	76°	17′.5

Add 360° to enable you		
to subtract the longitude	360°	
	436°	17′.5
Longitude W	− 132°	55′.0W
Local hour angle (LHA)	303°	22′.5
Declination for 1700	23°	16′.5 N

2 To find calculated CZX

[Latitude	10°	20′.0 S
Declination	23°	16′.5 N
Add	33°	36′.5]

Log vers. LHA 303° 22′.5	9.6531
Log cos. lat. 10°′.20	9.9929
Log cos. dec. 23° 16′.5	9.9631
	9.6091
Change to natural versine	0.4066
Nat.vers.lat. +	
diff.decl. 33° 36′.5	0.1672
	0.5738
Calculated ZX	64° 44′

3 To find observed zenith distance and intercept

Sextant altitude	25°	11′
Index error		− 1′.5
	25°	09′.5
Total correction		+ 10′.7
	25°	20′.2
	90°	00′
Observed zenith distance	64°	39′.8
Calculated zenith distance	64°	44′
Intercept		04′.2 (T)

[To name the intercept it might help to remember **A FOG** - which stands for *away from observed greater* - ie intercept is named away if the observed zenith distance is greater. If the observed zenith distance is less than the calculated, then the intercept must be named towards.]

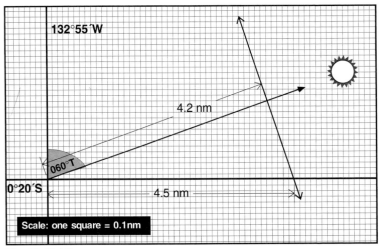

Fig 30 Plot 3

4 To find azimuth, or bearing
From ABC tables, using LHA, latitude and declination
A = .093 +
B = .502 +
C = .595
Az = N 59°.4E ≈ 060°True
(see Fig 30: from graph vessel is about 4.8 miles east of DR at 0815)

5 To find observed longtitude at 0815
Dlong = departure × secant latitude
Dlong = 4.8 x 1.02
    = 4.9 or 5′ of longtitude
Observed longitude at 0815 = 132° 50′ W

6 To find Noon DR Position
If possible, it is always best to draw this out on the chart; otherwise, on a piece of squared paper so that you can see what is happening. Using the new position at 0815 of 10° 20′ S, 132° 50′ W plot the course and distance of the vessel to noon, then transfer the 0815 position line through the noon DR position. In Fig 31, P1-L1 represents the transferred position line drawn through the noon DR. On this diagram the course and distance run gives a difference in

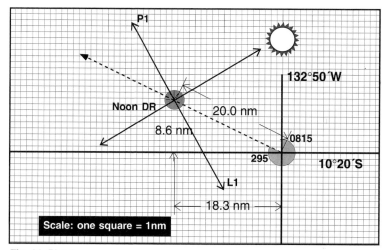

Fig 31 Plot 4

latitude of 8°.5′ further north and 18′ of departure further west.

So the noon DR will be: 10° 11′.5 S, 133° 08′ W.

This can also be worked out using the traverse tables. Bear in mind that if the vessel was in high latitudes the departure would have to be converted into minutes of longtitude.

7 To find latitude at noon

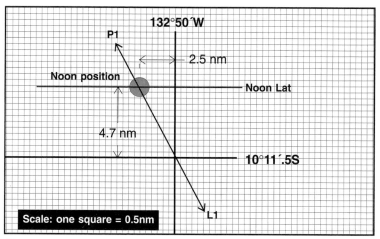

Fig 32 Plot 5

Time sun on meridian		
Transit	12	00 00
Longitude	8°	53′.28W
GMT	20hr	53min 28sec
Sextant altitude	56°	25′
Index error		− 1′.5
	56°	23′.5
Total correction		+ 12′.7
	56°	36′.2
	90°	00′.0
	33°	23′.8
	33°	24′.3
Declination	23°	17′.0 N
Latitude	10°	06′.8 S

The noon latitude puts vesssel 4.7 miles further north and about 2.5 miles further west, so observed noon position is:

Observed noon position = 10° 06′.8 S, 133° 52′.5 W

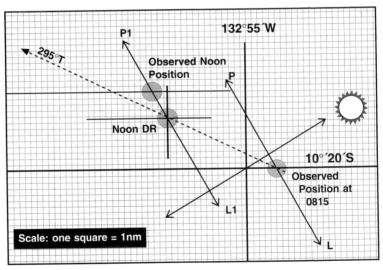

Fig 33 Plot 6

10

POSITION FIXING USING THE STARS AND PLANETS

Using the stars and planets will give you an absolute fix. If you are able to take four stars, or three stars and a planet, chosen so that they give you a good cross, you can obtain an accurate position. With the advent of the air tables, which give the bearing, or **azimuth**, of the star and the calculated altitude, it is easier and quicker than using the haversine formula and *Reed's*. (However, with practice, the formula can still be useful and some skippers may even prefer this method.)

Taking Star Sights

Star sights have to be taken at twilight, morning and evening, when the stars are visible and the horizon can also be seen. You will usually have about half an hour in which to take your sightings, a little longer in the higher latitudes. It is useful to know the approximate bearing of the star you are using and its altitude so that you can preset the angle on the sextant. This will make it easier to find the star and bring it down to the horizon. You will need a sextant with a good telescope.

A Bubble Sextant is a type of sextant with its own artificial horizon built in so that a position can be obtained from the stars at any time during the night or when the horizon is not clearly visible.

It is a good idea, if possible, to take four stars, as shown in Fig 34. It is unlikely that they will all cross exactly, but that you will end up with a diamond within which the vessel probably lies. The advantage of taking stars which have opposite, or nearly opposite, bearings is that they check each other and, as with the Sun, it is possible that the navigator will know which of the four sights taken was the best one.

The sights have to be taken in quick succession and the times recorded accurately. So, again, it is advisable to have a crew member recording the times for you as you take the sights.

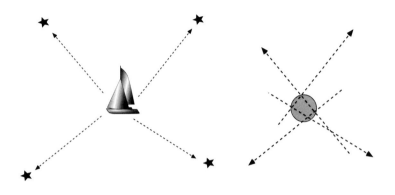

Fig 34 Four star position fix   **Fig 35** Most probable position

Star Charts

Star charts are available from good chandlers and they are an invaluable aid in helping to find the position of the important navigational stars and planets. Figs 36 and 37 are extracts from star charts showing the main stars used in navigation.

The brightest stars, those of the **first magnitude**, are the easiest to see and recognise. Sailing at night in the oceans, you will soon get used to these stars and their respective constellations as you encounter them nightly.

The Northern Hemisphere

On the star chart the numbered stars are as follows:

1 Apheratz	3 Schedar	7 Hamal	9 Menkar
27 Alphard	30 Denebois	44 Alphecca	
49 Rasalhague	50 Eltanin	57 Enif	60 Markab

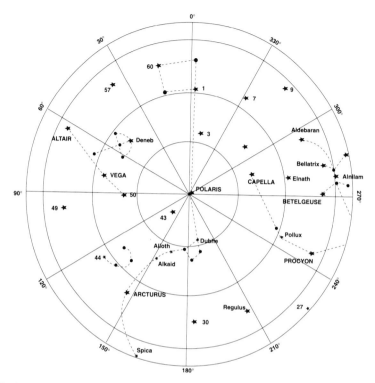

Fig 36 Star chart Northern Hemisphere

The Southern Hemisphere

On the Southern Hemisphere chart the numbered stars are as follows:

2 Ankaa	4 Diphda	8 Acamar	9 Menkar
25 Subail	26 Miaplacidus	27 Alphard	31 Gienah
39 Menkent	42 Zuben'ubi	46 Atria	47 Sabik
53 Nunki	57 Enif	58 AlNa'ir	

Stars of the first magnitude are marked in capital letters; stars of magnitude 2.0 to 1.0 are in small letters.

If you are using the Marq St Hilaire method and *Reed's* to work your star sights, it may be wise to devise a pro-forma on which to make your entries, with columns headed with the name of your chosen star.

67

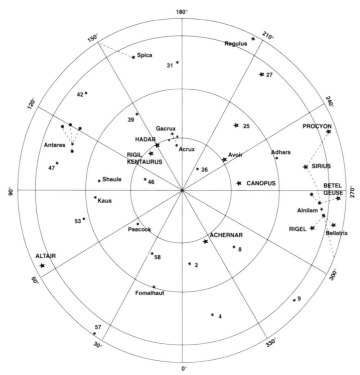

Fig 37 Star chart Southern Hemisphere

For example

[The following example is worked using both the Marq St Hilare method and the *Sight Reduction Tables*.]

On 5 May a vessel is in DR position 38° 50′.N, 42° 36′.W. At 0530, the following stars are observed:

Mirfak   sextant altitude 18° 31′   deck watch time 08h 18m 42s
Enif   sextant altitude 55° 48′.5   deck watch time 08h 20m 22s
Rasalhague
           sextant altitude 44° 31′   deck watch time 08h 21m 37s
Kochab   sextant altitude 39° 01′   deck watch time 08h 22m 56s
Index error: –2′.0.   Height of eye 10ft.
Find the vessel's position at 0530

1 To find local hour angle star (use Aries in nautical almanacs):

	MIRFAK	ENIF	RASALHAGUE	KOCHAB
GHA Aries	342° 56′.1	342° 56′.1	342° 56′.1	342° 56′.1
GHA corr	4° 41′.2	5° 06′.3	5° 25′.2	5° 44′.9
GHA Aries	347° 37′.3	348° 02′.4	348° 21′.3	348° 41′.0
SHA for star +	309° 05′.9	34° 04′.2	96° 22′.2	137° 17′.7
	656° 43′.2	382° 06′.6	444° 43′.5	485° 58′.7
−360	360°		360°	360°
	296° 43′.2	382° 06′.6	84° 43′.5	125° 58′.7
Longitude W−	42° 36′.0	42° 36′.0	42° 36′.0	42° 36′.0
LHA star	254° 07′.2	339° 30′.6	42° 07′.5	83° 22′.7

2 To find calculated zenith distance using versines and cosines:

	MIRFAK	ENIF	RASALHAGUE	KOCHAB
Log vers LHA	0.1050	8.8012	9.4121	0.9467
Log cos lat	9.8915	9.8915	9.8915	9.8915
Log cos decl	9.8096	9.9936	9.9895	9.4352
	9.8061	8.6863	9.2931	9.2734
Nat Versine	6400	0486	1964	1876
Nat Vers.lat/dec	0184	1254	1033	1845
	6584	1740	2997	3721
Calculated ZX	70°01′	34°18′.5	45°33′	51°06′

3 To find azimuths using ABC tables

	MIRFAK	ENIF	RASALHAGUE	KOCHAB
A =	0.232 −	02.17 +	0 .900 +	0 .100 +
B =	1.24 −	0.49 −	0 .318 −	2 .40 −
C =	1.472 −	1.68 −	0 .582 +	2 .30 −
Azimuth =	N43°E	S37°E	S65°W	N29°W

4 To find observed zenith distance and intercept

	MIRFAK	ENIF	RASALHAGUE	KOCHAB
Sextant Alt	20° 10′	55° 48′.5	44° 31′	39° 01′
Index Error	−2′.0	−2′.0	−2′.0	−2′.0
	20° 08′	55° 46′.5	44° 29′	38° 59′
Star Total Corr.	−6′	−5′	−4′	−4′
	20° 02′	55° 41′.5	44° 25′	38° 55′
	90° 00′	90° 00′	90° 00′	90° 00′
Observed ZX	69° 58′	34° 18′.5	45° 35′	51° 05′
Calculated ZX	70° 01′	34° 18′.5	45° 33′	51° 06′
Intercept	3T	0	2A	1T

5 Plot the position on the appropriate chart or by drawing to scale on squared paper (Fig 38):

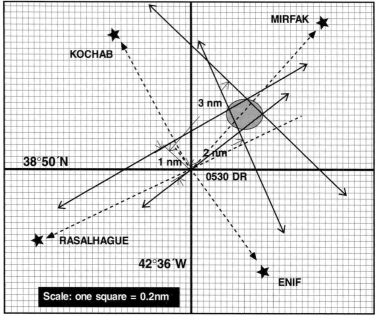

Fig 38 Plot 7

Position at 0530 is 38° 52′ N, 42° 34′ W.

The star position puts the vessel north and east of the DR: 2 miles north and 1.5 miles east, which is equal to 2 minutes of longitude.

In reality, it is unlikely that you will get complete agreement with the answer. Mathematical interpolation to the nearest 0′.1 is probably unnecessary; accuracy to the nearest 1′.0 may be more realistic.

Using Air Navigation Tables

The same example can be worked using the *Sight Reduction Tables*. These can be found in the Appendix at the back of this book.

	MIRFAK	ENIF	RASALHAGUE	KOCHAB
GHA Aries	342° 56'.1	342° 56'.1	342° 56'.1	342° 56'.1
GHA corr	4° 41'.2	5° 06'.3	5° 25'.2	5° 44'.9
GHA Aries	347° 37'.3	348° 02'.4	348° 21'.3	348° 41'.0
Chosen Long	42° 37'.3	42° 02'.4	42° 21'.3	42° 41'.0
W – LHA	305°	306°	306°	306°

Note: the SHA is not used when using the sight reduction tables

	MIRFAK	ENIF	RASALHAGUE	KOCHAB
	Hc Zn	Hc Zn	Hc Zn	Hc Zn
	20°05' 041	55°50' 143	44°12' 247	39°04' 340
Observed Alt	20°02	55°41'.5	44°25	38°55
Intercept	3A	8.5A	13A	9A

Plot a point 39° N,42° W on the squared paper.
Plot the chosen longtitudes converted to departure along the latitude line of 39° N. Draw the bearing from this point and plot

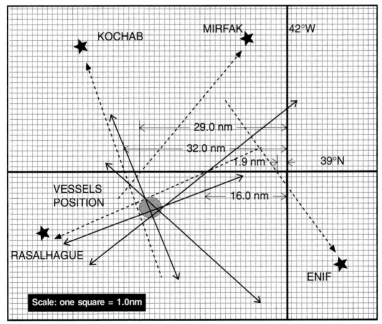

Fig 39 Plot 8

71

intercepts along bearing. Draw the position lines at right angles to the bearing. Where all the position lines meet is the position of the vessel. The departure (east/west distance has to be converted back to Dlong).

As the altitudes are used and not the zenith distance the intercept has to be the same 'd' opposite to that used for the Marq St Hilaire method. If you are using A FOG as a memory then Away if the observed is the greater becomes *towards*.

11

USE OF THE MOON

As a heavenly body to use to find a position, the Moon has three distinct disadvantages:

1. It moves very quickly in the heavens so that great accuracy is required when taking a sight
2. The phases of the Moon do not give a total upper or lower limb
3. Intricate interpolation of the tables is required to achieve accuracy.

If it is essential to establish a position and there is no alternative, the Moon can be used in conjunction with a star sight fix or, if it is in the right position in the sky, a fix can be obtained with the Sun and the Moon during daylight hours. It is recommended that you check as soon as possible by some other means the position thus obtained.

Information in Nautical Almanacs

You will find that the Moon has its own separate tables, with columns for each month showing, for every six hours, the Greenwich Hour Angle and declination. A further column shows the mean variation per hour for each 14° + minutes. Other tables show the corrections for GHA and declination. A total correction table is also given for each limb. The almanac will also show the dates of the phases of the Moon and times of moonrise and moonset.

Obtaining a Position Line

This can be done either by using the Marq St Hilaire method or by using the *Sight Reduction Tables for Air Navigation.*

For example

A vessel is in DR position 37° 25′ N, 24° 52′ W, on 4 October. At 1830 ship's time an observation of the lower limb of the Moon was made. The sextant altitude of the lower limb was 10° 50′ and deck watch time was 20hr 05min 16sec, which was correct with GMT. Height of eye was 8ft, index error 2′.0 on the arc. Find the intercept and azimuth.

1 Find LHA

GHA for 1800	271°	33′.2	var 29′.1
For 2hr	28°	58′.0	
For 05min	1°	12′.4	
For 16sec		3′.9	
For 20° 05′.16 GHA	301°	47′.5	
Longitude	24°	52′.0W	
LHA	276°	55′.5	

[to find declination:

for 1800	10°	07′.3N
for 2hr		30′.4
for 05min		1′.4
Declination	10°	39′.1N]

2 Find Calculated ZX

Versine LHA (P) =	9.9442	
Log cos lat	9.9000	
Log cos decl	9.9925	
	9.8367	
Nat vers	0.6866	
Nat vers lat diff decl	0.1070	
	0.7936	

Calculated ZX =	78°	04′

[Lat	37°	25′ N
Decl	10°	39′.1N
Lat/Decl	26°	44′.9]

3   To find observed zenith distance

Sextant altitude	10°	50′.0
Index error		2′.0
	10°	48′.0
Total correction	1°	00′.0
[Horizontal parallax 59.8]		
Height of eye correction		7′.0
	11°	55′.0
	90°	00′
Observed zenith distance	78°	05′

4   To find intercept and azimuth

Calculated zenith distance	78°	04′
Observed zenith distance	78°	05′
Intercept		01′ Away

A = .092 +
B = .178 −
C = .086
Az = N 86° E

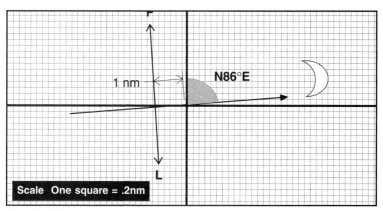

1 nm   N86°E

L

Scale One square = .2nm

Fig 40 Plot 9

The above plot indicates that the vessel is about 1′ west of the DR position. However, all the corrections for the Moon make the exercise rather tedious and it is unlikely that you would use it in practice. The same exercise can be done with the *Sight Reduction for Air Navigation Tables.*

12

CHECKING THE COMPASS

The magnetic compass is still the primary means of navigating small craft across the oceans. Larger vessels are fitted with gyro compasses, but it is unusual to find one of these in a small boat. The compass is therefore the most important instrument on your boat. Before you begin an ocean voyage, you should be confident that your compass is reliable and it should be thoroughly checked for any error. Even so, you should always carry a spare on board in case the main compass gets damaged or becomes unreliable.

The compass should be checked for any **deviation**, and a deviation curve should be drawn showing the deviation for different headings. Do check from time to time that no metal object is being kept near the compass and that your helmsman is not affecting it in any way.

Care must be taken if the vessel is heeled over for any length of

Fig 41 Compass bowl

time, as **heeling error** can occur, particularly in steel-built craft. This will be detected when the compass is checked for error.

An air bubble in the compass bowl will adversely affect its working. Compass bowls are filled with a mixture of alcohol and distilled water. (The alcohol is added to reduce the freezing point of the mixture.) You may find that your compass has a filling hole; if this is the case, you can remove the bubble by topping up the compass with distilled water. Keep going until it overflows and then replace the screw.

Checking compass error

Amplitude   The error of the compass can be checked each sunrise and sunset by taking a compass bearing of the Sun and comparing it with the true bearing obtained from the amplitude tables. All you need to know is the approximate latitude of your vessel and the declination of the Sun to the nearest degree. The true bearing can be read directly from the table in the almanac.

For example
On 10 June, in latitude 35°N, declination 23°N, the Sun rose bearing 085° by the compass. The variation from the chart was 20°W. Find the deviation. (see Figs 42 and 43).

Sun's true bearing from table	N 61°.5 E
Compass bearing	N 85°.0 E
Error	23°.5 W
Variation	20°.0 W
Deviation	3°.5 W

Azimuth   It is a good idea to check the compass each time you take a morning or afternoon sight. In fact, you can only do this when the Sun is fairly low in the sky, below about fifty degrees. At other times it is very difficult to get an accurate compass bearing.

If you take a bearing of the Sun immediately after taking its sextant altitude, you will be able to compare the compass bearing with the true bearing, as given in the air tables under the heading Z. If you are using *Reed's*, you will have to consult the ABC tables to find the true azimuth at the time of taking the bearing.

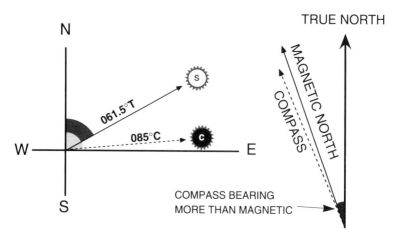

Fig 42 Checking compass

Fig 43 Calculating deviation

For Example

On 12 June a vessel is in DR position 42° 15′ N, 5° 15′E. At 0830 a Sun sight is taken. At the same time the sun bore 093°(C). Deck watch time is 08hr 19min 22sec. Find the compass error and the deviation, if the variation is 10°E.

GHA for 0800	300°	04′.2
Correction	4°	50′.5
	304°	54′.7
Longitude	5°	15′ E
LHA	310°	09′.7

From ABC tables:
A = .756 +   Declination 23°08′N
B = .528 –
C = .228
Azimuth = S 80°7 E

True bearing	099°(T)	Variation 10°E
Compass bearing	093°(C)	Deviation 4°W
Error	6° E	

Also at the same time the Sun bore 093°(C)

From *Sight Reduction Tables for Air Navigation*:

Latitude same name as declination

LHA of 310° gives Z as 099°

Example 2

A vessel is in DR position 50° 22′ N, 10° 25′ W on 2 October. At 1530 ship's time an observed altitude of the Sun was taken. A compass bearing of the Sun taken at the same time was 255°(C). If the deck watch time was 16hr 12min 42sec and the variation was 10°W, find the error on the compass.

GHA 1600	62°	59′.5	Declination 3° 39′ S
Corr. for 12min 42sec	3°	10′.5	
	65°	50′.0	
Longitude	10°	25′.0W	
LHA	55°	25′.0	

From *ABC* tables:

A = .835 +

B = .064 +

C = .899

Azimuth = S 60°.0 W = 240°

Compass Error   15°W

From *Sight Reduction Tables*:

Latitude different name to declination

LHA of 55° gives Z as 120.5. From small print at top of page (LHA less than 180° Zn = 360–Z).

$$\begin{array}{r} 360 \\ - 120.5 \\ \hline \end{array}$$

Azimuth =   239.5.

Ocean Magnetic Variation and Deviation

You have to remember that while crossing the oceans you will often be steering the same course for a long time. In this case, the deviation will not change, but the value of the variation may change daily. For example, if you are crossing the Atlantic Ocean, the variation may change from about 5°W in the English Channel to about

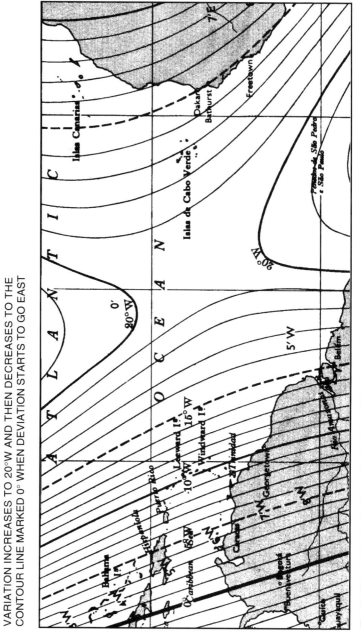

VARIATION INCREASES TO 20°W AND THEN DECREASES TO THE
CONTOUR LINE MARKED 0° WHEN DEVIATION STARTS TO GO EAST

Fig 44 Extract Admiralty Magnetic Variation Chart

20° W if you are heading towards the West Indies, more if you are heading further north.

It is wise to carry a chart of the area in which you are planning to sail which shows lines of magnetic variation. The chart on which you work will show the present variation, with the correction for the year.

Magnetic Anomalies

From time to time disturbances of the Earth's magnetic field occur which may, in turn, cause unknown errors of the compass. Such disturbances can be caused by:

1   magnetic storms, or
2   local attraction.

Magnetic storms, often accompanied by displays of the Aurora Borealis, usually cause only fleeting disturbances.

Local attraction occurs when a mass of magnetic ore or a wreck lies close enough to cause an error on the compass. The local pilot books will inform you of any such problem areas. One of the most remarkable areas of magnetic activity is off Western Australia where the variation has been observed to swing from 56°E to 26°W within a distance of 200 metres. The west coast of Scotland is also renowned for its local magnetic anomalies.

The chart reproduced in Fig 44 shows curves of equal magnetic variation for the North Atlantic Ocean. As can be seen, the variation increases to a maximum of about 20°W, decreasing again as you travel further west.

13

GREAT CIRCLE SAILING

As every schoolchild knows, the shortest distance between two places is a straight line, but on the surface of the Earth the line is, of course, curved, and the vessel will sail along an arc of the curve. Great circle sailing is used when you are travelling over large distances on the oceans and will save you many miles of sailing if you take the shortest curve to reach your destination.

For example, if you are sailing from Panama to New Zealand, the distance will be shorter if you sail a great circle route rather than a **Mercator** route. If you were crossing the Atlantic from New York to the English Channel, the shortest route would be a great circle route north-about rather than a direct Mercator route.

A vessel in the diagram below sailing the northern route would find it a shorter distance than the southern route.

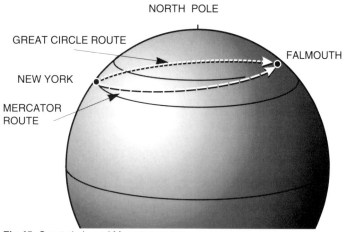

Fig 45 Great circle and Mercator routes

82

If a vessel follows a great circle track, the course has to be altered continually as a curve is being followed. In practice, the track is divided into suitable lengths: a series of **rhumb lines**. Rhumb lines are straight lines drawn on a gnomic chart. So in Fig 46, when travelling from A to E there are four separate courses to be steered. Point X on the diagram is called the **vertex** and is the point where the great circle route is nearest to the pole. This point is important, as there may be a northern or southern limit, depending upon which ocean you are in, beyond which you do not wish to pass north or south because of some hazard, such as ice.

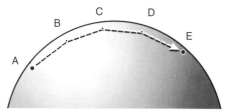

Fig 46 Great circle track

A great circle is, by definition, a circle on the Earth's surface with the centre of the Earth as its centre, so it may be that sometimes a composite great circle route has to be used to avoid danger areas. Looking at Fig 47, a vessel leaving A would travel on great circle AC and then join great circle EB to avoid going north of C, eventually reaching the destination at B.

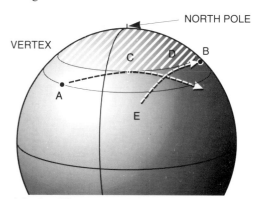

Fig 47 Passage following different great circles

The Gnomic Chart

The projection of the gnomic chart is designed to help navigators to find great circle tracks by drawing straight lines on the chart. A straight line drawn from A to B on the chart will, in fact, represent a great circle route (Fig 48). To find points A, B, C, D and E on the chart, you have to make a note of the approximate latitude and plot this position on the Mercator chart with the longitude. You can then find out your course for that particular leg of the passage.

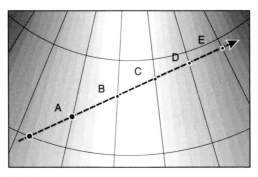

Fig 48 The gnomic chart

On a gnomic chart, great circles appear as straight lines and rhumb lines appear curved. Meridians are straight lines which converge at the poles. Parallels of latitude are curves.

Mercator Sailing

Most charts are produced on the Mercator projection, where lines of longitude and latitude are straight. This causes distortion in the higher latitudes. Mercator sailing is used for finding courses to steer and distances to go over long distances: more than 500 miles. The traverse tables in *Reed's* are only accurate up to a distance of 500 miles; after that Mercator sailing must be used.

Mercator sailing is preferred when the course is mainly northerly or southerly, as there will be no advantage to be gained from great circle sailing.

Mercator sailing is right-angled plane trigonometry where the

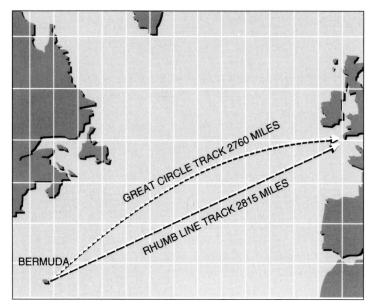

Fig 49 Mercator Projection

difference in latitude, difference in longitude, departure (distance in nautical miles in an east-west direction), distance and course are used.

You may, for example, wish to sail a course direct from the English Channel to the Cape Verde Islands, a distance of some 2,375 nautical miles.

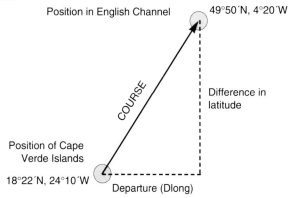

Fig 50 Difference between routes

English Channel	49° 50′N	4° 20′W
Cape Verde Ils.	18° 22′N	24° 10′W
	31° 28′	19° 50′

Difference in latitude = 31° 28′

31°28′ = 31 × 60 = 1860 + 28 = Dlat of 1888 nautical miles

Difference in longitude = 19° 50′

19° 50′ = 19 × 60 = 1140 + 50 = 1190 minutes of Dlong.

Because of the distortion of the Mercator chart, to get an accurate answer we have to consider a unit called a **meridional part**. This provides a unit of measurement so that we can directly link the minute of longitude to the minute of latitude. The meridional parts of any latitude are the number of units of longitude in the length of a meridian between the parallel of that latitude and the equator.
Meridional parts can be found in nautical tables, *Nories'* or *Burton's*.

So, to find the course:

$$Tan\ course = \frac{Dlong}{DMP}\ (difference\ of\ meridional\ parts)$$

Distance = Dlat × secant course.

The Traverse Tables

The traverse tables given in *Reed's* will only give courses and distances up to two-hundred miles. In larger nautical tables such as *Nories'*, they are accurate up to five-hundred miles.

The tables consist of the solution of right-angled triangles which are based on difference of latitude, departure, difference in longitude course and distance. You can find any of these from this table.

For Example
Find the course and distance from 49° 22′ N, 5° 07′ W, to 48° 08′N, 6° 22′ W.

Latitude from	49°	22′	Longtitude from	5°	07′ W
Latitude to	48°	08′	Longtitude to	6°	22′ W
Dlat	1°	14′		1°	15′
	× 60 = 74′			× 60 = 75′	

We need to convert the Dlong into departure:
  departure = Dlong × cos lat (we use mean lat)
  Departure = 75 × cos 49 = 75 × 0.66 = 49.5

Look through the table to find where a departure of 49.5 coincides with a Dlat of 74. The nearest is Dlat 75.5 and dep 49.0 which gives a distance of 90 miles and a course of 33° which, if you consider which way the vessel is sailing, ie south and west, the vessel is making more southing than westing so the course must be S 33°W or 213°T.

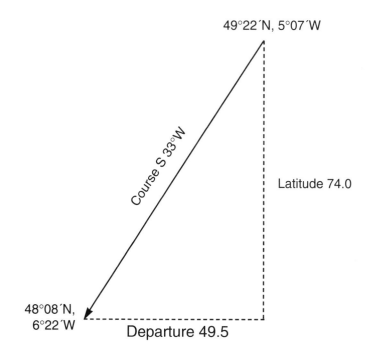

49°22′N, 5°07′W

Course S 33°W

Latitude 74.0

48°08′N,
6°22′W

Departure 49.5

Fig 51 Course direction diagram

By drawing a simple diagram it can be seen whether the south-north distance is greater or smaller than the east-west distance.

14
ELECTRONIC NAVIGATION

When all else fails, you will be able to use the sextant. In spite of modern technology, electronic aids sometimes do not work. But it has to be said that, if they are working, then you will be able to get regular positions across the oceans with great ease. Merely by pushing a few buttons, your latitude or longitude will be displayed clearly and accurately to within a few metres.

For the navigator it is obviously a great advantage that a lot of time does not have to be spent on mathematical computations; instead, the boat can be sailed on its best course with the most suitable sails set. You will be able to plot your position on the chart with accuracy as often as you wish, and correct your course accordingly.

Satellite Navigation

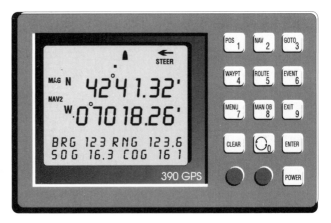

Fig 52 Modern electronic navigation aid

Navigation by means of signals bounced off a chain of satelites has now been in use for some years, and it is being improved all the time. The **Global Positioning System** (GPS) is the latest in position fixing technology. This system provides a position at almost any time you want one, anywhere on the globe, to the nearest few metres. As time goes on, the electronic instruments will become more and more reliable. With just a few small batteries you will be able to navigate your boat worldwide.

THIS IS THE LATEST IN GPS
NAVIGATION.

IT IS WATERPROOF AND CAN
FLOAT.

IT IS EASY TO USE AND HAS
ITS OWN
SMALL BATTERIES.

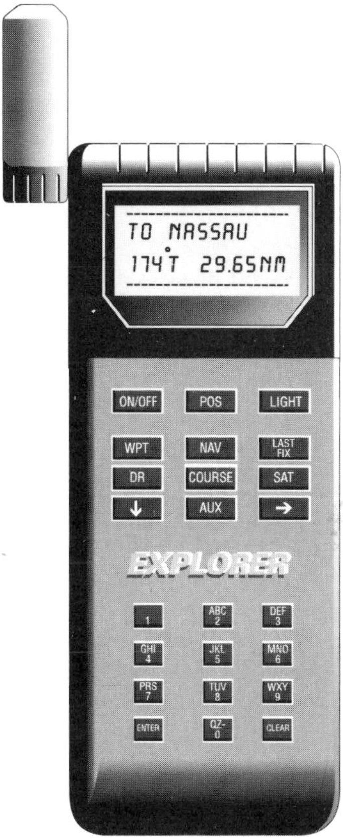

Fig 53 Hand held Satnav receiver

Decca and Loran

For inshore waters, Decca is still very popular. It will only give positions while you are in the Decca chain, which covers this country and parts of the Mediterranean. It was thought that it was going to be superceded by Loran, but this has now been put back some years.

Loran is an American development, and the present Loran C is more successful than the original Loran A. The waters covered are the North Atlantic, North Pacific and the Mediterranean. It has a range of about two thousand miles and is accurate to about five hundred metres on a lesser range than one thousand miles.

THIS SMALL PIECE OF EQUIPMENT CAN BE PROGRAMMED
TO USE DECCA, LORAN OR SATNAV

Fig 54 Multi purpose receiver

Radio Beacons (RDF)

Radio beacons can still be a good guide when approaching land. These are listed in the *Admiralty Book of Radio Signals*. You may still be able to use a radio direction-finder to pick up these signals and obtain a guide to your position if you have no other means of finding out.

15

OCEAN METEOROLOGY

Generally, the weather in the oceans tends to be more settled than that experienced over land masses. When you are sailing, you are likely to be in a trade wind belt or a westerly wind belt where the wind blows from a constant direction nearly every day. Once you leave the Bay of Biscay and reach the North East Trade Winds, they will carry you southwards to about ten degrees from the equator, sometimes even further south. The accompanying weather tends to be the same, with blue skies and occasional cloud. However, visibility can change as a result of local conditions, such as sand reducing visibility in the prevailing North East Trades off the west coast of Africa.

There are large areas of high pressure in the oceans which are usually best avoided as they are areas of very little wind. In the days of sail, vessels would become becalmed for days on end and, because of dwindling water supplies, would have to jettison any horses on board. This was such a frequent occurence that these latitudes became known as the **horse latitudes**.

As an ocean mariner, you need to be aware of the general weather patterns around the world: where the high and low pressure systems are; the likelihood of **tropical revolving storms**; local winds such as the **Föhn** winds experienced in the Mediterranean.

Remember that weather patterns usually move with the Sun so, for example, the Azores high moves further north in the northern summer and then recedes again with the southward movement of the Sun. The weather patterns around the equator also move north and south with the Sun, as do the trade winds.

World Weather System

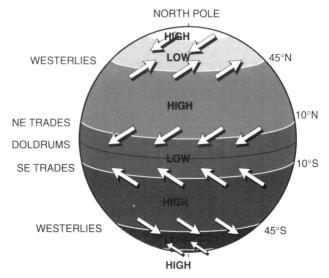

Fig 55 World wind and pressure system

The above diagram indicates the general wind and pressure system over the surface of the Earth. Winds blow from a high pressure area to a low pressure area, so from the figure the trade winds can be seen to blow from the high to the low near the equator. They vary in strength depending on the time of year.

The North Atlantic is covered with westerly winds called the **Westerly Variables**. In the South Atlantic, because there is no land to break up the wind pattern, the **Roaring Forties** blow without relenting at all in those latitudes, and sometimes even become the **Furious Fifties**.

The rotation of the Earth is responsible for deflecting the winds from merely blowing due north or south. As can be seen, the trade winds blow from the north east or the south east.

World Weather Patterns

There are well established weather patterns covering the globe dependent on the high and low pressure systems. By comparing the next two charts the differences between a northern winter and summer are clearly shown. The first shows the distribution of pressure and winds for the northern winter. Note the development of the high pressure over Asia, which causes the **North East Monsoon** to blow in winter. Now look at the next drawing, Fig 57, which shows the distribution of pressure and winds for the northern summer. Note how the pressure has changed to a low over Asia, resulting in the **South West Monsoon**.

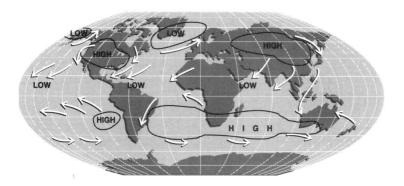

Fig 56 Northern winter

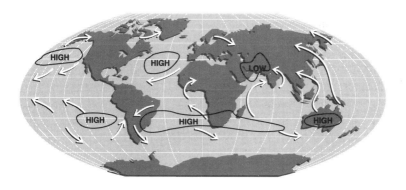

Fig 57 Northern summer

Wind Direction

Pressure and winds are linked meteorologically: low pressure will have winds blowing into the low whereas a high pressure area will have winds blowing out of it. In summer, low pressure areas develop over land masses because of the rapid heating of the land compared to the sea. This can result in very strong winds locally, the monsoon winds being extreme examples. The cause is, in fact, the same as that which results in the pleasant sea breeze experienced on a warm summer's day.

Local Weather Patterns

Admiralty pilot books are a useful source of information on local weather patterns. You will find such topics covered as wind speed, temperature, days with fog, amounts of cloud, humidity and rainfall. Should you happen to be sailing off the east coast of South America, for example, there is a strong wind called the **Pamero** which is fully described. An important point for small boat sailors noted in the pilot is that once this local phenomenon is established it is not always associated with bad weather.

Ocean Currents

Ocean currents tend to follow the general pattern of the winds. For example, the **Gulf Stream**, which becomes the westerly **Wind Drift** current in the northern Atlantic, is partly the result of the prevailing westerly winds. The winds help to keep the currents moving, and when the winds bring warm air, the ocean currents bring warm water as well. In the lower latitudes of the North Atlantic, surface water is driven westwards by the trade winds; it passes through the Caribbean and emerges near Florida as the Gulf Stream. And so the westerly drift of water is warm and is still warm when it reaches, the shores of northwest Europe.

Certain currents bring with them their own dangers: of ice, fog or large waves. The **Labrador Current**, off the east coast of Canada, brings down ice from the Arctic. When it meets the warm water of the Gulf Stream, dense fog is formed. Fog and ice form a potentially lethal combination for any ship, even the *Titanic.*

It is warm air from the Gulf Stream flowing over the cold waters from the Arctic which cause such dense and widespread fog.

At the equator, currents follow the general flow of wind. However, south of the westward-moving current, a counter-current flows in the opposite direction. Within a few miles, therefore, the current could be flowing eastwards.

Ocean currents can flow up to about two knots, and probably average a drift of about thirty to fifty miles a day. Currents will be stronger round large peninsulas, such as the Cape of Good Hope, where the **Agulhas Current** can flow up to four or five knots.

The monsoon winds can set up their own currents. South of Sri Lanka, the counter equatorial current may be as much as three knots during the South West Monsoon.

The ocean navigator needs to know the currents which are likely to be experienced during the voyage, so you are advised to study the various charts and diagrams which show you the currents of the world and the rates at which they flow. The major ocean currents of the world are shown in Fig 58 As you can see, they follow the main wind patterns and flow round the high and low pressure areas of the world.

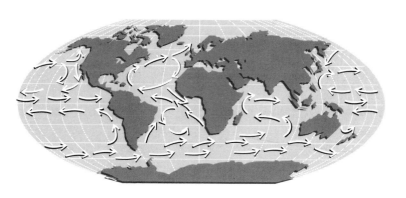

Fig 58 World ocean currents

Ocean Weather Forecasts

The Meteorological Office at Bracknell, Berkshire, provides forecasts for all areas of the world. For instance, forecasts for the North Atlantic, up to 40° west, are given out daily at 0930 and 2130 GMT from Portishead Radio. Forecasts for this area can be obtained at any time by giving your name and call sign, the forecast period and area required, to the nearest coast radio station, or you can telephone 0344 420242.

The Meteorological Office also has Metroute, a worldwide weather forecasting and routeing system for yachts and other small craft. This will cost you a little money but may be worthwhile. Information can be obtained from the Meteorological Office, London Road, Bracknell, Berkshire RG12 2SZ (Telephone: 0344 854904/5).

Tropical Revolving Storms

In ocean sailing, perhaps the most feared of the elements that might be encountered is the tropical revolving storm. It is unlikely that a small boat would survive the experience. Even large vessels have been badly damaged, or sunk, by these storms: in 1944 three American destroyers were caught in a typhoon in the Pacific and sunk, with the loss of nearly eight hundred crew.

Tropical storms occur mainly on the western and equatorial sides of the high pressure systems, in the Arabian Sea, the Bay of Bengal, the south east Indian Ocean, off the north west coast of Australia and off the west coast of Central America. They are unknown in the South Atlantic.

What tropical storms are called varies according to the region in which they occur, ie:

Western North Atlantic	Hurricanes
Eastern North Pacific	Hurricanes
South Pacific	Hurricanes
Western North Pacific	Typhoons
Indian Ocean	Cyclones
Bay of Bengal	Cyclones
Arabian Sea	Cyclones
North West Australia	Willy-willies

The storms occur most frequently during the late summer and early autumn of the hemisphere. They are rare in the southern hemisphere from mid-May to November and in the northern hemisphere from mid-November to mid-June. In the Arabian Sea, storms occur at the change of the monsoon.

Various publications record the average number of tropical revolving storms which occur over a period. The sort of figures that might be shown for a sample year are:

West Indies	5
Western North Pacific	25
Western South Pacific	3
Southern Indian Ocean	6
Bay of Bengal	2
Arabian Sea	1
Eastern North Pacific	3
West coast of Australia	1

In any one year, these figures can vary by up to fifty per cent.

Storm Tracks

The storms originate about ten degrees north of the equator and move off in a north-westerly direction, in the northern hemisphere. When they reach a latitude of about twenty degrees north, they **recurve** and head off in a north-easterly direction.

In the southern hemisphere they move off in a south-westerly direction and recurve in about latitude twenty degrees south, moving off again in a south-easterly direction.

To begin with, the speed of the storm is about ten knots, but this will increase to twenty to twenty-five knots after recurvature. The extent of the storm, with hurricane force winds, is not likely to be much more than two hundred miles. Once storms have recurved, they usually degenerate into **temperate latitude depressions.**

Below is some useful terminology connected with tropical revolving storms:

Vertex: the most westerly point reached by the storm

Vortex: the centre, or eye, of the storm

Dangerous quadrant: the leading quadrant of the storm - to be avoided at all costs!

Dangerous semi-circle: the side which lies on the side of the recurvature and could blow the vessel into the path of the storm

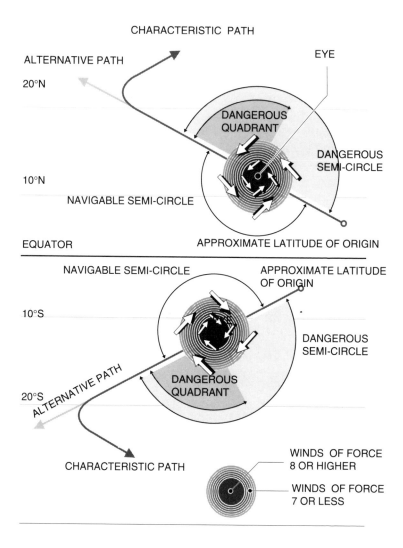

CHARACTERISTIC PATH

ALTERNATIVE PATH

EYE

20°N

DANGEROUS
QUADRANT

DANGEROUS
SEMI-CIRCLE

10°N

NAVIGABLE SEMI-CIRCLE

EQUATOR

APPROXIMATE LATITUDE OF ORIGIN

NAVIGABLE SEMI-CIRCLE

APPROXIMATE LATITUDE
OF ORIGIN

10°S

DANGEROUS
SEMI-CIRCLE

DANGEROUS
QUADRANT

20°S
ALTERNATIVE PATH

CHARACTERISTIC PATH

WINDS OF FORCE
8 OR HIGHER

WINDS OF FORCE
7 OR LESS

Fig 59 Tropical revolving storms

Navigable semi-circle: the side of the storm away from the recurvature. If you are in this semi-circle you will tend to get blown away from the centre of the storm.

98

Warning Signs

Barometric Pressure   At sea in the tropics, the barometric pressure
hardly changes from day to day, but on the approach of a storm the
barometer will become unsteady and show a slow fall about five
hundred miles from the centre of the storm. A distinct fall occurs
about one hundred miles from the centre, while at about fifty miles
the fall in barometric pressure is rapid. At the rear of the storm the
pressure rises as quickly as it fell.

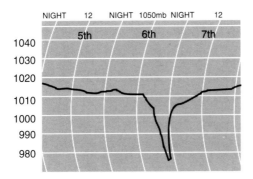

Fig 60   Barometric trace of tropical storm

Swell   Another indication of the approach of a tropical revolving
storm is the swell. The swell can extend up to a thousand miles
from the centre of the storm and may give a good idea of the
bearing of the centre.

Wind Direction and Clouds   A change of wind direction may also
indicate the approach of a storm, as also may a change in the
appearance of the sky: a 'v' formation of cirrus clouds can indicate
a storm's approach.

Taking Evasive Action

If you suspect that a tropical revolving storm is approaching, you
need to use all the information at your disposal to try and evade it.
Weather forecasts will give you a good idea of the position of the
storm, as these phenomena are tracked and reported in detail but,
even with all the information to hand, it is sometimes impossible to

predict the course a storm will take, as they are liable to sudden changes of path. There are rules for avoiding a storm. You need to know:

1   the bearing of the centre of the storm
2   the path of the storm
3   whether your vessel is in the dangerous or the navigable semi-circle

Buys Ballot's Law will help you decide on the bearing of a storm. If you stand facing the wind, the centre of the storm will be about ninety degrees on your right side in the northern hemisphere and on your left hand side in the southern hemisphere.

You will be at risk if you pass closer than two hundred miles to the centre of the storm. If you are in the northern hemisphere and the wind is veering, then you will be in the dangerous semi-circle. If this is the case, you should heave to on the starboard tack and haul round to starboard as the wind veers.

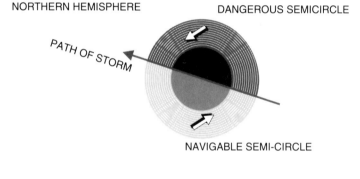

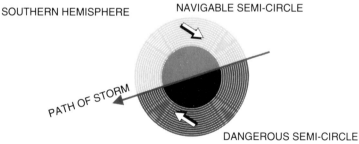

Fig 61   Dangerous semi-circles

If the wind remains steady in direction, then the vessel is in the path of the storm and you should run before the wind with the wind on your starboard quarter and alter course to port when the wind backs.

If you are in the southern hemisphere, the vessel must be in the dangerous semi-circle and you should heave to on the port tack and haul round to port as the wind backs. If the wind remains steady, then you are in the path of the storm and you should run with the wind on your port quarter and alter course to starboard as the wind veers (see Fig 61).

Hurricane Holes

There are certain harbours around the world, noted in pilot books, as places where you can sit out such severe storms though it would be foolish to suggest that you will not suffer any damage even in such favoured locations. If you are in harbour, it will be prudent to seek as much shelter as possible and secure the vessel as strongly as you can. It will probably help if you head your vessel towards the centre of the storm. Remember that the height of the tide will increase, possibly rising by an extra fifteen feet or more, and that storm waves of large dimensions will occur.

16
OCEAN PASSAGE PLANNING

Planning an ocean voyage can take many months of enquiries and accumulation of information. You will need to plan your route thoroughly, note all the places you intend to visit and acquire all the relevant information about them. You may be planning to go in company with other yachts, but you will still need your own comprehensively worked-out plans.

The Boat

The boat you choose for your voyage must be one in which you have every confidence and one which you know very well. If it is a boat that you have had for some time, the rigging and deck fixtures may need strengthening. The hull must be sound and every opening must be checked for any signs of weakness.

Consideration should be given to the construction of the hull, whether to choose GRP, concrete, wood or steel. If you are planning to sail among coral reefs, for example, it may be wise to contemplate a steel hull which does not damage as easily as GRP. The type of rig may be dependent on the number of crew sailing with you. Two masts can give you smaller sails which are easier to handle, and, if one breaks, you have another to sail with. A ketch rig may, therefore, be a good option.

You may also consider altering the accommodation below such that in an emergency you can separate the bow from the main cabin by means of a watertight door as an added safety factor.

Stores, Fuel and Water

Planning an ocean voyage means that you have to have adequate supplies for the period of the longest passage at sea, plus some in reserve. It is wise to make comprehensive lists of what you require and, once purchased, to store the items on the boat well-labelled and in some sort of order.

You will probably want to carry extra fuel to help you move out of windless areas. Careful thought must be given to the stowage of all fuel.

Each member of the crew will need at least one pint of water each day just to survive, so you will be able to calculate how much water you need. A person can survive about ten times as long without food as without water, so enough water is vital.

The Crew

You need to choose your crew carefully. You need to know that you will all get on together and that you have as many experienced and qualified crew members as possible.

Safety

All aspects of safety must be considered, and a list of equipment drawn up. Basic items such as lifejackets, lifebuoys and lights should be in good order and there should be sufficient for all on board. Safety harnesses should be checked, as should pyrotechnics, fire extinguishers and fire blankets.

You will have to rig a safety line from forward to aft on both sides of the vessel and of sufficient strength to take the full weight of a falling crew member when attached to it by their safety harness.

The life raft must have been recently serviced and should be stowed in the correct place - away from all hazards, such as rigging. On a vessel of sufficient size, aft of the cockpit is as good a place as any.

Make sure that all on board know about all aspects of safety including how to launch a liferaft and how to get in it, the correct radio procedure for sending out a distress call, and how to fire off flares upwards and not down into the cockpit. Courses on the use of liferafts are held at frequent intervals at recognising training centres and are well worth attending.

Publications

You will need the following publications on board:

Charts of the areas in which you plan to sail
A nautical almanac
Admiralty pilots
Admiralty tide tables
Gnomic charts
Routeing charts
Admiralty list of lights
Admiralty list of radio signals
International code of signals
Tidal stream atlas
Nautical tables/air tables
Ocean Passages of the World

Customs Regulations

You will need on board documents proving ownership of the vessel, ie bill of sale, builder's certificate, registration documents. You will also, of course, need passports for all the crew. Don't forget to fill in customs forms before you leave indicating where your voyage is going to take you.

Procedures in Foreign Ports

If you wish to have as few problems with officials as possible then try to follow local customs. A chat with another sailor can provide valuable information, even whether to avoid a particular port completely. Always fly the courtesy flag of the country you are entering at the correct position, and the right way up! Some local areas have their own flags in addition to the nationality flag. If you can manage to acquire one of these as well, preferably cheaply from other sailors returning from the same area, flying a local flag can help smooth progress when registering your arrival with the relevant authorities (there may be more than one office to visit).

Consult the harbourmaster for moorings, or for any other information about local and customs regulations.

17
NAUTICAL ALMANACS
AND NAUTICAL TABLES

There is a wealth of published information for the would-be astro navigator, so much so that it is bewildering trying to make the right choice. The various volumes are not cheap. Some volumes may cover one year, others ten years, and others contain information that never changes. It is important to establish the difference between nautical tables and nautical almanacs.

Nautical Almanacs

There are three almanacs which contain the information you need about the Sun, stars, planets and Moon: *Reed's*, *Macmillan's* and the *Admiralty Nautical Almanac* (Yachtsman's Edition).

Nautical Tables

Again you have a choice of three which contain all the necessary mathematical tables required: *Nories'*, *Burton's* and *Reed's Nautical Almanac.*

Air Navigation Tables

The *Sight Reduction Tables for Air Navigation* are also used for astro navigation. They consist of the calculated altitude, not the calculated zenith distance, calculated for all latitudes and all declinations. They indicate which star is available for certain Local Hour Angles and give azimuths for each heavenly body for the required LHA. The criteria used are LHA, latitude and declination. You have to be careful that you use the right page and make sure that either latitude and declination are the same name, or have different names. You still need one of the nautical almanacs to be able to navigate.

Nautical Almanacs

Reed's Nautical Almanac   This almanac contains all the tables required to navigate a vessel across the oceans using a sextant.

The Admiralty Nautical Almanac   Contains only the annual information of the movement and positions of all heavenly bodies. A set of mathematical nautical tables is also required to do the calculations for astro-navigation.

Yachtsman Nautical Almanac   Contains all information on the movement and position of heavenly bodies, but for astro-navigation work nautical mathematical tables are also required.

Macmillan & Silk Cut Nautical Almanac   Contains movement and position of heavenly bodies and tables for use of calculator to obtain position by astro-navigation.

Nautical Tables

Nories' Nautical Tables   Mathematical tables containing all data necessary for calculations in astro-navigation. They have to be used in conjunction with a nautical almanac.

Burton's Nautical Tables   A similar set of tables with the same limitations.

Using Reed's Almanac

All the information you require, including mathematical tables, can be found in *Reed's Nautical Almanac*. Most of the exercises in this book have been based on using *Reed's*. It is important therefore to understand how to use the various tables and what they mean. The following tables have to be used for calculations in astro-navigation:

1   The monthly ephemeris tables for obtaining GHA and declination
2   The Sun or stars altitude correction table
3   The versine table
4   The cosine table
5   The traverse table
6   The departure into Dlong table
7   The ABC table
8   The GHA correction table

When these tables are fully understood, the computation of astro-navigation is relatively simple.

The Monthly Ephemeris Table

☉ SUN — January,

G.M.T.	SUN		ARIES	G.M.T.	SUN		ARIES
	G.H.A.	Dec.	G.H.A.		G.H.A.	Dec.	G.H.A.

	Friday, 1st January				**Wednesday, 6th January**		
h	° ′	° ′	° ′	h	° ′	° ′	° ′
00	179 08.5	S23 01.1	100 39.5	00	178 34.2	S22 31.1	105 35.1
02	209 07.9	23 00.7	130 44.4	02	208 33.7	22 30.5	135 40.1
04	239 07.3	23 00.2	160 49.3	04	238 33.1	22 29.9	165 45.0
06	269 06.7	22 59.8	190 54.2	06	268 32.6	22 29.3	195 49.9
08	299 06.1	22 59.4	220 59.2	08	298 32.0	22 28.7	225 54.9
10	329 05.5	22 59.0	251 04.1	10	328 31.5	22 28.1	255 59.8
12	359 04.9	22 58.6	281 09.0	12	358 30.9	22 27.5	286 04.7
14	29 04.3	22 58.1	311 14.0	14	28 30.4	22 26.9	316 09.6
16	59 03.7	22 57.7	341 18.9	16	58 29.8	22 26.3	346 14.6
18	89 03.2	22 57.3	11 23.8	18	88 29.3	22 25.7	16 19.5
20	119 02.6	22 56.9	41 28.7	20	118 28.8	22 25.0	46 24.4
22	149 02.0	S22 56.4	71 33.7	22	148 28.2	S22 24.4	76 29.4

Fig 62 Ephemeris tables.

The GHA and declination of the Sun are given daily, for two-hourly intervals. The GHA of Aries (for use with stars) is also given on the same line. Care must be taken, when reading the declination of the Sun, to note whether it is north or south.

The GHA and declination for the stars are given: each month on its own page. If using the Marq St Hilaire method, the SHA of the stars is also given.

Information is also given on the Sun, times of transit, times of twilight, sunset and sunrise for each day of the month. The same information is given for the Moon and for the planets,

Sun's Altitude Correction Table

This table is headed with the height of the observer's eye in metres or feet and, down the left-hand side of the page, the observed altitude from the sextant. The correction is always additive. At the foot of the page can be found a small monthly correction, which must also be applied.

The star or planet altitude correction tables are used in the same way, except that the correction is always subtractive.

The Versine Table

	42°		43°		44°		45°		46°		47°	
I	LOG.	NAT.	LOG.	NAT.	LOG.	NAT.	LOG.	NAT	LOG.	NAT.	LOG.	NAT
0	9.4097	0.2569	4292	2686	9.4482	2807	4667	2929	9.4848	3053	5024	3180
1	9.4100	0.2570	4295	2688	9.4485	2809	4670	2931	9.4851	3056	5027	3182
2	9.4103	0.2572	4298	2690	9.4488	2811	4673	2933	9.4854	3058	5030	3184
3	9.4107	0.2574	4301	2692	9.4491	2813	4676	2935	9.4857	3060	5033	3186
4	9.4110	0.2576	4305	2694	9.4494	2815	4679	2937	9.4860	3062	5036	3189
5	9.4113	0.2578	4308	2696	9.4497	2817	4682	2939	9.4863	3064	5039	3191
6	9.4117	0.2580	4311	2698	9.4501	2819	4685	2941	9.4866	3066	5042	3193
7	9.4120	0.2582	4314	2700	9.4504	2821	4688	2943	9.4869	3068	5045	3195
8	9.4123	0.2584	4317	2702	9.4507	2823	4691	2945	9.4872	3070	5048	3197
9	9.4126	0.2586	4321	2704	9.4510	2825	4694	2947	9.4875	3072	5050	3199
10	9.4130	0.2588	4324	2706	9.4513	2827	4698	2950	9.4878	3074	5053	3201
11	9.4133	0.2590	4327	2708	9.4516	2829	4701	2952	9.4881	3076	5056	3203
12	9.4136	0.2592	4330	2710	9.4519	2831	4704	2954	9.4883	3079	5059	3206
13	9.4140	0.2594	4333	2712	9.4522	2833	4707	2956	9.4886	3081	5062	3208
14	9.4143	0.2596	4337	2714	9.4525	2835	4710	2958	9.4889	3083	5065	3210
15	9.4146	0.2598	4340	2716	9.4529	2837	4713	2960	9.4892	3085	5068	3212
16	9.4149	0.2600	4343	2718	9.4532	2839	4716	2962	9.4895	3087	5071	3214
17	9.4153	0.2602	4346	2720	9.4535	2841	4719	2964	9.4898	3089	5074	3216
18	9.4156	0.2604	4349	2722	9.4538	2843	4722	2966	9.4901	3091	5076	3218
19	9.4159	0.2606	4352	2724	9.4541	2845	4725	2968	9.4904	3093	5079	3221
20	9.4162	0.2608	4356	2726	9.4544	2847	4728	2970	9.4907	3095	5082	3223
21	9.4166	0.2610	4359	2728	9.4547	2849	4731	2972	9.4910	3097	5085	3225
22	9.4169	0.2612	4362	2730	9.4550	2851	4734	2974	9.4913	3100	5088	3227
23	9.4172	0.2613	4365	2732	9.4553	2853	4737	2976	9.4916	3102	5091	3229
24	9.4175	0.2615	4368	2734	9.4556	2855	4740	2978	9.4919	3104	5094	3231
25	9.4179	0.2617	4372	2736	9.4560	2857	4743	2981	9.4922	3106	5097	3233
26	9.4182	0.2619	4375	2738	9.4563	2959	4746	2983	9.4925	3108	5099	3236
27	9.4185	0.2621	4378	2740	9.4566	2861	4749	2985	9.4928	3110	5102	3238
28	9.4188	0.	91	2742	9.4569	2863	4752		9.4931	3112	5105	3240
29	9.4192			2744	9.4572	2865	47		4934	3114	5108	3242
30	9		4438		9.4575	2867		3024	9	3116	5111	3
		0.2659						3024	9			
	250	0.2661	4441	276			4809	3026	9.498		51	
	9.4253	0.2663	4444	2782		4	4812	3028	9.4989	3		3283
49	9.4256	0.2665	4447	2784	9.463	2906	4815	3030	9.4992	3157	5	3285
50	9.4260	0.2667	4450	2786	9.4637	2908	4818	3033	9.4995	3159	5168	3287
51	9.4263	0.2669	4454	2788	9.4640	2910	4821	3035	9.4998	3161	5171	3289
52	9.4266	0.2671	4457	2790	9.4643	2912	4824	3037	9.5001	3163	5174	3291
53	9.4269	0.2673	4460	2792	9.4646	2915	4827	3039	9.5004	3165	5177	3294
54	9.4273	0.2675	4463	2794	9.4649	2917	4830	3041	9.5007	3167	5180	3296
55	9.4276	0.2677	4466	2797	9.4652	2919	4833	3043	9.5010	3169	5182	3298
56	9.4279	0.2679	4469	2799	9.4655	2921	4836	3045	9.5013	3172	5185	3300
57	9.4282	0.2681	4472	2801	9.4658	2923	4839	3047	9.5016	3174	5188	3302
58	9.4285	0.2682	4476	2803	9.4661	2925	4842	3049	9.5018	3176	5191	3304
59	9.4289	0.2684	4479	2805	9.4664	2927	4845	3051	9.5021	3178	5194	3307
60	9.4292	0.2686	4482	2807	9.4667	2929	4848	3053	9.5024	3180	5197	3309

	LOG.	NAT.	LOG.	NAT.	LOG.	NAT.	LOG.	NAT	LOG.	NAT.	LOG.	NAT.
	317°		**316°**		**315°**		**314°**		**313°**		**312°**	

Fig 63 Versine table

This table has degrees along the top (0-179) and bottom (180-359), with minutes reading down the left-hand side and up the right-hand side (see Fig 63). If using degrees from the top of the page, the left-hand minutes should be used; if using degrees from the bottom of the page, the right-hand minutes should be used.

Each degree has two columns: the darker type shows the log versine; the lighter type shows the natural versine. Take note of the number before the decimal point in the log versines to determine whether it is 9. or 8.

To solve the PZX triangle, it is necessary to find the log versine of the LHA. To this must be added the log cosine of the latitude and the log cosine of the declination.

The Cosine Table

′	30°	31°	32°	33°	34°	35°	36°	37°	38°	39°	40°	41°	42°
0	9.9375	9331	9284	9236	9186	9.9134	9080	9023	8965	9.8905	8843	8778	8711
1	9.9375	9330	9283	9235	9185	9.9133	9079	9023	8964	9.8904	8841	8777	8710
2	9.9374	9329	9283	9234	9184	9.9132	9078	9022	8963	9.8903	8840	8776	8708
3	9.9373	9328	9282	9233	9183	9.9131	9077	9021	8962	9.8902	8839	8775	8707
4	9.9372	9328	9281	9233	9182	9.9130	9076	9020	8961	9.8901	8838	8773	8706
5	9.9372	9327	9280	9232	9181	9.9129	9075	9019	8960	9.8900	8837	8772	8705
6	9.9371	9326	9279	9231	9181	9.9128	9074	9018	8959	9.8899	8836	8771	8704
7	9.9370	9325	9279	9230	9180	9.9127	9073	9017	8958	9.8898	8835	8770	8703
8	9.9369	9325	9278	9229	9179	9.9127	9072	9016	8957	9.8897	8834	8769	8702
9	9.9369	9324	9277	9229	9178	9.9126	9071	9015	8956	9.8896	8833	8768	8700
10	9.9368	9323	9276	9228	9177	9.9125	9070	9014	8955	9.8895	8832	8767	8699
11	9.9367	9322	9275	9227	9176	9.9124	9069	9013	8954	9.8894	8831	8766	8698
12	9.9367	9322	9275	9226	9175	9.9123	9069	9012	8953	9.8893	8830	8763	8696
13	9.9366	9321	9274	9225	9175	9.9122	9068	9011	8952	9.8892	8829	8763	8696
14	9.9365	9320	9273	9224	9174	9.9121	9067	9010	8951	9.8891	8828	8762	8695
15	9.9364	9319	9272	9224	9173	9.9120	9066	9009	8950	9.8890	8827	8761	8694
16	9.9364	9318	9272	9223	9172	9.9119	9065	9008	8949	9.8889	8825	8760	8692
17	9.9363	9318	9271	9222	9171	9.9119	9064	9007	8948	9.8888	8824	8759	8691
18	9.9362	9317	9270	9221	9170	9.9118	9063	9006	8947	9.8887	8823	8758	8690
19	9.9361	9316	9269	9220	9169	9.9117	9062	9005	8946	9.8885	8822	8757	8689
20	9.9361	9315	9268	9219	9169	9.9116	9061	9004	8945	9.8884	8821	8756	8688
21	9.9360	9315	9268	9219	9168	9.9115	9060	9003	8944	9.8883	8820	8755	8687
22	9.9359	9314	9267	9218	9167	9.9114	9059	9002	8943	9.8882	8819	8753	8686
23	9.9358	9313	9266	9217	9166	9.9113	9058	9001	8942	9.8881	8818	8752	8684
24	9.9358	9312	9265	9216	9165	9.9112	9057	9000	8941	9.8880	8817	8751	8683
25	9.9357	9312	9264	9215	9164	9.9111	9056	9000	8940	9.8879	8816	8750	8682

Fig 64 Cosine table

The log cosine table has degrees at the top and minutes down the left-hand side of the page (see Fig 64). It is necessary to find the log cosine of the latitude and the log cosine of the declination. You will find that, in most cases, the log will be prefixed with a 9.

The Traverse Table

COURSE	21' D.Lat	21' Dep	22' D.Lat	22' Dep	23' D.Lat	23' Dep	24' D.Lat	24' Dep	25' D.Lat	25' Dep	26' D.Lat	26' Dep	27' D.Lat	27' Dep	28' D.Lat	28' Dep	29' D.Lat	29' Dep	COURSE
0	21.0	0.0	22.0	0.0	23.0	0.0	24.0	0.0	25.0	0.0	26.0	0.0	27.0	0.0	28.0	0.0	29.0	0.0	90
1	21.0	0.4	22.0	0.4	23.0	0.4	24.0	0.4	25.0	0.4	26.0	0.5	27.0	0.5	28.0	0.5	29.0	0.5	89
2	21.0	0.7	22.0	0.8	23.0	0.8	24.0	0.8	25.0	0.9	26.0	0.9	27.0	0.9	28.0	1.0	29.0	1.0	88
3	21.0	1.1	22.0	1.2	23.0	1.2	24.0	1.3	25.0	1.3	26.0	1.4	27.0	1.4	28.0	1.5	29.0	1.5	87
4	20.9	1.5	21.9	1.5	22.9	1.6	23.9	1.7	24.9	1.7	25.9	1.8	26.9	1.9	27.9	2.0	28.9	2.0	86
5	20.9	1.8	21.9	1.9	22.9	2.0	23.9	2.1	24.9	2.2	25.9	2.3	26.9	2.4	27.9	2.4	28.9	2.5	85
6	20.9	2.2	21.9	2.3	22.9	2.4	23.9	2.5	24.9	2.6	25.9	2.7	26.9	2.8	27.8	2.9	28.8	3.0	84
7	20.8	2.6	21.8	2.7	22.8	2.8	23.8	2.9	24.8	3.0	25.8	3.2	26.8	3.3	27.8	3.4	28.8	3.5	83
8	20.8	2.9	21.8	3.1	22.8	3.2	23.8	3.3	24.8	3.5	25.7	3.6	26.7	3.8	27.7	3.9	28.7	4.0	82
9	20.7	3.3	21.7	3.4	22.7	3.6	23.7	3.8	24.7	3.9	25.7	4.1	26.7	4.2	27.7	4.4	28.6	4.5	81
10	20.7	3.6	21.7	3.8	22.7	4.0	23.6	4.2	24.6	4.3	25.6	4.5	26.6	4.7	27.6	4.9	28.6	5.0	80
11	20.6	4.0	21.6	4.2	22.6	4.4	23.6	4.6	24.5	4.8	25.5	5.0	26.5	5.2	27.5	5.3	28.5	5.5	79
12	20.5	4.4	21.5	4.6	22.5	4.8	23.5	5.0	24.5	5.2	25.4	5.4	26.4	5.6	27.4	5.8	28.4	6.0	78
13	20.5	4.7	21.4	4.9	22.4	5.2	23.4	5.4	24.4	5.6	25.3	5.8	26.3	6.1	27.3	6.3	28.3	6.5	77
14	20.4	5.1	21.3	5.3	22.3	5.6	23.3	5.8	24.3	6.0	25.2	6.3	26.2	6.5	27.2	6.8	28.1	7.0	76
15	20.3	5.4	21.3	5.7	22.2	6.0	23.2	6.2	24.1	6.5	25.1	6.7	26.1	7.0	27.0	7.2	28.0	7.5	75
16	20.2	5.8	21.1	6.1	22.1	6.3	23.1	6.6	24.0	6.9	25.0	7.2	26.0	7.4	26.9	7.7	27.9	8.0	74
17	20.1	6.1	21.0	6.4	22.0	6.7	23.0	7.0	23.9	7.3	24.9	7.6	25.8	7.9	26.8	8.2	27.7	8.5	73
18	20.0	6.5	20.9	6.8	21.9	7.1	22.8	7.4	23.8	7.7	24.7	8.0	25.7	8.3	26.6	8.7	27.6	9.0	72
19	19.9	6.8	20.8	7.2	21.7	7.5	22.7	7.8	23.6	8.1	24.6	8.5	25.5	8.8	26.5	9.1	27.4	9.4	71
20	19.7	7.2	20.7	7.5	21.6	7.9	22.6	8.2	23.5	8.6	24.4	8.9	25.4	9.2	26.3	9.6	27.3	9.9	70
21	19.6	7.5	20.5	7.9	21.5	8.2	22.4	8.6	23.3	9.0	24.3	9.3	25.2	9.7	26.1	10.0	27.1	10.4	69
22	19.5	7.9	20.4	8.2	21.3	8.6	22.3	9.0	23.2	9.4	24.1	9.7	25.0	10.1	26.0	10.5	26.9	10.9	68
23	19.3	8.2	20.3	8.6	21.2	9.0	22.1	9.4	23.0	9.8	23.9	10.2	24.9	10.5	25.8	10.9	26.7	11.3	67
24	19.2	8.5	20.1	8.9	21.0	9.4	21.9	9.8	22.8	10.2	23.8	10.6	24.7	11.0	25.6	11.4	26.5	11.8	66
25	19.0	8.9	19.9	9.3	20.8	9.7	21.8	10.1	22.7	10.6	23.6	11.0	24.5	11.4	25.4	11.8	26.3	12.3	65
26	18.9	9.2	19.8	9.6	20.7	10.1	21.6	10.5	22.5	11.0	23.4	11.4	24.3	11.8	25.2	12.3	26.1	12.7	64
27	18.7	9.5	19.6	10.0	20.5	10.4	21.4	10.9	22.3	11.3	23.2	11.8	24.1	12.3	24.9	12.7	25.8	13.2	63
28	18.5	9.9	19.4	10.3	20.3	10.8	21.2	11.3	22.1	11.7	23.0	12.2	23.8	12.7	24.7	13.1	25.6	13.6	62
29	18.4	10.2	19.2	10.7	20.1	11.2	21.0	11.6	21.9	12.1	22.7	12.6	23.6	13.1	24.5	13.6	25.4	14.1	61
30	18.2	10.5	19.1	11.0	19.9	11.5	20.8	12.0	21.7	12.5	22.5	13.0	23.4	13.5	24.2	14.0	25.1	14.5	60
31	18.0	10.8	18.9	11.3	19.7	11.8	20.6	12.4	21.4	12.9	22.3	13.4	23.1	13.9	24.0	14.4	24.9	14.9	59
32	17.8	11.1	18.7	11.7	19.5	12.2	20.4	12.7	21.2	13.2	22.0	13.8	22.9	14.3	23.7	14.8	24.6	15.4	58
33	17.6	11.4	18.5	12.0	19.3	12.5	20.1	13.1	21.0	13.6	21.8	14.2	22.6	14.7	23.5	15.2	24.3	15.8	57
34	17.4	11.7	18.2	12.3	19.1	12.9	19.9	13.4	20.7	14.0	21.6	14.5	22.4	15.1	23.2	15.7	24.0	16.2	56
35	17.2	12.0	18.0	12.6	18.8	13.2	19.7	13.8	20.5	14.3	21.3	14.9	22.1	15.5	22.9	16.1	23.8	16.6	55
36	17.0	12.3	17.8	12.9	18.6	13.5	19.4	14.1	20.2	14.7	21.0	15.3	21.8	15.9	22.7	16.5	23.5	17.0	54
37	16.8	12.6	17.6	13.2	18.4	13.8	19.2	14.4	20.0	15.0	20.8	15.6	21.6	16.2	22.4	16.9	23.2	17.5	53
38	16.5	12.9	17.3	13.5	18.1	14.2	18.9	14.8	19.7	15.4	20.5	16.0	21.3	16.6	22.1	17.2	22.8	17.9	52
39	16.3	13.2	17.1	13.8	17.9	14.5	18.7	15.1	19.4	15.7	20.2	16.4	21.0	17.0	21.8	17.6	22.5	18.3	51
40	16.1	13.5	16.9	14.1	17.6	14.8	18.4	15.4	19.2	16.1	19.9	16.7	20.7	17.4	21.4	18.0	22.2	18.6	50
41	15.8	13.8	16.6	14.4	17.4	15.1	18.1	15.7	18.9	16.4	19.6	17.1	20.4	17.7	21.1	18.4	21.9	19.0	49
42	15.6	14.1	16.3	14.7	17.1	15.4	17.8	16.1	18.6	16.7	19.3	17.4	20.1	18.1	20.8	18.7	21.6	19.4	48
43	15.4	14.3	16.1	15.0	16.8	15.7	17.6	16.4	18.3	17.0	19.0	17.7	19.7	18.4	20.5	19.1	21.2	19.8	47
44	15.1	14.6	15.8	15.3	16.5	16.0	17.3	16.7	18.0	17.4	18.7	18.1	19.4	18.8	20.1	19.5	20.9	20.1	46
45	14.8	14.8	15.6	15.6	16.3	16.3	17.0	17.0	17.7	17.7	18.4	18.4	19.1	19.1	19.8	19.8	20.5	20.5	45

| | Dep | D.Lat | Dep | D.Lat | Dep | D.Lat | Dep | D.Lat | Dep | D.Lat | Dep | D.Lat | Dep | D.Lat | Dep | D.Lat | Dep | D.Lat | |
| | 21' | | 22' | | 23' | | 24' | | 25' | | 26' | | 27' | | 28' | | 29' | | COURSE |

DISTANCE

Fig 65 Traverse table

This table is used to ascertain the position a vessel would reach if it maintained a particular course over a given time and distance. It is generally used to find the noon DR position from the morning sights. The table (Fig 65) has distance along the top and bottom of the page, while the course steered reads down the left-hand side or up the right-hand side of the page. The courses specified only cover one quadrant, from 0°– 90°, so you will have to convert your three figure course to a quadrantal course, eg a course of 120° becomes S60°E, as from the bottom of the page the Dlat is smaller than the departure.

The traverse table can be used for distances up to 200 miles. It gives the Dlat in minutes of latitude the vessel will have travelled and the departure (east-west direction) the vessel has travelled. The departure has to be converted into Dlong (difference of longitude).

The Departure into Dlong Table

VICE VERSA

Dep=D. Long Cos. Mean Lat.
D. Long. = Dep. Sec. Lat.

MEAN LAT	COS. LAT	SEC. LAT
0.00	1.00	1.00
5.00	1.00	1.00
10.00	0.98	1.02
12.00	0.98	1.02
14.00	0.97	1.03
15.00	0.97	1.04
16.00	0.96	1.04
17.00	0.96	1.05
18.00	0.95	1.05
19.00	0.95	1.06
20.00	0.94	1.06
21.00	0.93	1.07
22.00	0.93	1.08
23.00	0.92	1.09
24.00	0.91	1.09
25.00	0.91	1.10
26.00	0.90	1.11
27.00	0.89	1.12
28.00	0.88	1.13
29.00	0.87	1.14
30.00	0.87	1.15
31.00	0.86	1.17
32.00	0.85	1.18
33.00	0.84	1.19
34.00	0.83	1.21
35.00	0.82	1.22
36.00	0.81	1.24
37.00	0.80	1.25
38.00	0.79	1.27

Fig 66 Departure into Dlong table

111

The east-west distance (departure) in miles has to be converted into minutes of longitude. Because lines of longitude converge towards the poles, the further north or south you are the greater the difference between the departure and the Dlong. The table in *Reed's* (Fig 66) shows that in latitude 50° you have to multiply the departure by 1.56 to get the Dlong. This happens to be the secant of latitude 50.

The ABC Tables

These tables are used to find the bearing of the Sun at the time of taking the sight, or for the bearing of any other heavenly body. They are a little complex and have to be interpolated, but you do not have to be too accurate.

A HOUR ANGLE at top **+**

Hour angle at bottom **—**

LAT	32° 328°	34° 326°	36° 324°	38° 322°	40° 320°	42° 318°	44° 316°	46° 314°	48° 312°	50° 310°	52° 308°	54° 306°
0°	.000	000	000	000	000	000	000	000	000	000	000	000
3	.084	078	072	067	062	058	054	051	047	044	041	038
6	168	156	145	135	125	117	109	101	095	088	082	076
9	253	235	218	203	189	176	164	153	143	133	124	115
12	340	315	293	272	253	236	220	205	191	178	166	154
15	429	397	369	343	319	298	277	259	241	225	209	195
18	520	482	447	416	387	361	336	314	293	273	254	236
21	614	569	528	491	457	426	398	371	346	322	300	279
24	713	660	613	570	531	494	461	430	401	374	348	323
27	.815	755	701	652	607	566	528	492	459	428	398	370
30	.924	.856	.795	739	688	641	598	558	520	484	451	419
33	1.04	.963	894	831	774	721	672	627	585	545	507	472
36	1.16	1.08	1.00	930	866	807	752	702	654	610	568	528
38	1.25	1.16	1.08	1.00	931	868	809	754	703	656	610	568
40	1.34	1.24	1.15	1.07	1.00	932	869	810	756	704	656	610
42	1.44	1.33	1.24	1.15	1.07	1.00	932	870	811	756	703	654
44	1.55	1.43	1.33	1.24	1.15	1.07	1.00	933	870	810	754	702
46	1.66	1.54	1.43	1.33	1.23	1.15	1.07	1.00	932	869	809	752
48	1.78	1.65	1.53	1.42	1.32	1.23	1.15	1.07	1.00	932	868	807
50	1.91	1.77	1.64	1.53	1.42	1.32	1.23	1.15	1.07	1.00	.931	866
52	2.05	1.90	1.76	1.64	1.53	1.42	1.33	1.24	1.15	1.07	1.00	930
54	2.20	2.04	1.89	1.76	1.64	1.53	1.43	1.33	1.24	1.15	1.08	1.00
56	2.37	2.20	2.04	1.90	1.77	1.65	1.54	1.43	1.33	1.24	1.16	1.08
58	2.56	2.37	2.20	2.05	1.91	1.78	1.66	1.55	1.44	1.34	1.25	1.16
60	2.77	2.57	2.38	2.22	2.06	1.92	1.79	1.67	1.56	1.45	1.35	1.26
62	3.01	2.79	2.59	2.41	2.24	2.09	1.95	1.82	1.69	1.58	1.47	1.37
64	3.28	3.04	2.82	2.62	2.44	2.28	2.12	1.98	1.85	1.72	1.60	1.49
66	3.59	3.33	3.09	2.87	2.68	2.49	2.33	2.17	2.02	1.88	1.75	1.63
LAT	148° 212°	146° 214°	144° 216°	142° 218°	140° 220°	138° 222°	136° 224°	134° 226°	132° 228°	130° 230°	128° 232°	126° 234°

Fig 67 Table A

112

B Lat. and Dec. SAME NAME —
Lat. and Dec. DIFFERENT NAMES +

DEC	32° 328°	34° 326°	36° 324°	38° 322°	40° 320°	42° 318°	44° 316°	46° 314°	48° 312°	50° 310°	52° 308°	54° 306°
0°	000	000	000	000	000	000	000	000	000	000	000	000
3	.099	.094	.089	.085	.082	.078	.075	.073	.071	.068	.067	065
6	.198	.188	.179	.171	.164	.157	.151	.146	.141	.137	.133	130
9	.299	.283	.269	.257	.246	.237	.228	.220	.213	.207	.201	196
12	.401	.380	.362	.345	.331	.318	.306	.295	.286	.277	.270	263
15	.506	.479	.456	.435	.417	.400	.386	.372	.361	.350	.340	331
18	.613	.581	.553	.528	.505	.486	.468	.452	.437	.424	.412	402
21	.724	.686	.653	.623	.597	.574	.553	.534	.517	.501	.487	474
24	.840	.796	.757	.723	.693	.665	.641	.619	.599	.581	.565	550
27	.962	.911	.867	.828	.793	.761	.733	.708	.686	.665	.647	630
30	1.09	1.03	.982	.938	.898	.863	.831	.803	.777	.754	.733	714
33	1.23	1.16	1.11	1.05	1.01	.971	.935	.903	.874	.848	.824	803
36	1.37	1.30	1.24	1.18	1.13	1.09	1.05	1.01	.978	.948	.922	898
38	1.47	1.40	1.33	1.27	1.22	1.17	1.12	1.09	1.05	1.02	.991	966
40	1.58	1.50	1.43	1.36	1.31	1.25	1.21	1.17	1.13	1.10	1.06	1.04
42	1.70	1.61	1.53	1.46	1.40	1.35	1.30	1.25	1.21	1.18	1.14	1.11
44	1.82	1.73	1.64	1.57	1.50	1.44	1.39	1.34	1.30	1.26	1.23	1.19
46	1.95	1.85	1.76	1.68	1.61	1.55	1.49	1.44	1.39	1.35	1.31	1.28
48	2.10	1.99	1.89	1.80	1.73	1.66	1.60	1.54	1.49	1.45	1.41	1.37
50	2.25	2.13	2.03	1.94	1.85	1.78	1.72	1.66	1.60	1.56	1.51	1.47
52	2.42	2.29	2.18	2.08	1.99	1.91	1.84	1.78	1.72	1.67	1.62	1.58
54	2.60	2.46	2.34	2.24	2.14	2.06	1.98	1.91	1.85	1.80	1.75	1.70
56	2.80	2.65	2.52	2.41	2.31	2.22	2.13	2.06	2.00	1.94	1.88	1.83
58	3.02	2.86	2.72	2.60	2.49	2.39	2.30	2.22	2.15	2.09	2.03	1.98
60	3.27	3.10	2.95	2.81	2.69	2.59	2.49	2.41	2.33	2.26	2.20	2.14
62	3.55	3.36	3.20	3.05	2.93	2.81	2.71	2.61	2.53	2.46	2.39	2.32
DEC	148° 212°	146° 214°	144° 216°	142° 218°	140° 220°	138° 222°	136° 224°	134° 226°	132° 228°	130° 230°	128° 232°	126° 234°

Fig 68 Table B

The combination of tables A and B refers you to Table C which, in turn, gives you the azimuth, or the bearing.

Read carefully how A and B are named. Table C is headed with the result of A plus or minus B, with latitude down the left-hand side. To name the azimuth, look carefully at the instructions at the foot of the page. Table C appears overleaf.

C = A ± B

AZIMUTH

C CORRECTION

Lat.	.00	.05	.10	.15	.20	.25	.30	.35	.40	.45	.50	.55	.60	.70	.80	.90	1.00	1.10	1.20	1.40	1.60	Lat.
0	90.0	87.1	84.3	81.5	78.7	76.0	73.3	70.7	68.2	65.8	63.4	61.2	59.0	55.0	51.3	48.0	45.0	42.3	39.8	35.5	32.0	0
10	90.0	87.2	84.6	81.6	78.9	76.2	73.5	71.0	68.5	66.1	63.8	61.6	59.4	55.4	51.8	48.4	45.4	42.7	40.2	36.0	32.6	10
20	90.0	87.3	84.6	82.2	79.4	76.8	74.2	71.8	69.0	67.1	64.8	62.6	60.4	56.4	52.7	49.8	46.6	44.1	41.6	37.2	33.6	20
24	90.0	87.4	84.8	82.2	79.6	77.6	74.7	72.3	69.9	67.6	65.3	63.3	61.3	57.3	53.8	50.6	47.6	44.9	42.4	38.0	34.3	24
28	90.0	87.5	85.0	82.5	80.0	77.6	75.2	72.8	70.5	68.3	66.2	64.1	62.1	58.3	54.8	51.5	48.6	45.8	43.3	39.0	35.3	28
30	90.0	87.5	85.1	82.6	80.2	77.8	75.4	73.1	70.9	68.7	66.6	64.5	62.5	58.8	55.3	52.1	49.1	46.4	43.9	39.5	35.8	30
32	90.0	87.6	85.2	82.8	80.4	78.0	75.7	73.5	71.2	69.1	67.0	65.0	63.0	59.3	55.9	52.7	49.7	47.0	44.5	40.1	36.4	32
34	90.0	87.6	85.3	82.8	80.6	78.3	76.0	73.8	71.7	69.5	67.5	65.6	63.6	59.9	56.4	53.3	50.3	47.6	45.1	40.7	37.0	34
36	90.0	87.7	85.4	83.1	80.8	78.6	76.4	74.2	72.1	70.0	68.0	66.0	64.1	60.5	57.1	53.9	51.0	48.3	45.8	41.4	37.7	36
38	90.0	87.7	85.5	83.3	81.0	78.9	76.7	74.6	72.6	70.5	68.5	66.6	64.7	61.1	57.8	54.7	51.8	49.1	46.6	42.2	38.4	38
40	90.0	87.8	85.6	83.4	81.3	79.2	77.1	75.0	73.0	71.0	69.0	67.2	65.3	61.8	58.5	55.4	52.5	49.9	47.4	43.0	39.2	40
42	90.0	87.9	85.8	83.6	81.5	79.5	77.4	75.4	73.4	71.5	69.6	67.8	66.0	62.5	59.3	56.2	53.4	50.7	48.3	43.9	40.1	42
44	90.0	87.9	85.9	83.8	81.8	79.8	77.8	75.9	73.9	72.0	70.2	68.4	66.7	63.3	60.1	57.1	54.2	51.6	49.2	44.8	41.0	44
46	90.0	88.0	86.0	84.1	82.1	80.1	78.2	76.3	74.5	72.6	70.8	69.1	67.4	64.1	60.9	57.9	55.2	52.6	50.2	45.8	42.0	46
48	90.0	88.1	86.2	84.3	82.4	80.5	78.6	76.8	75.0	73.2	71.5	69.8	68.1	64.9	61.8	58.9	56.2	53.6	51.2	46.9	43.0	48
50	90.0	88.2	86.3	84.5	82.7	80.9	79.0	77.3	75.6	73.9	72.2	70.5	68.9	65.7	62.8	60.0	57.3	54.7	52.4	48.0	44.2	50
52	90.0	88.3	86.5	84.7	83.0	81.2	79.5	77.8	76.2	74.4	72.9	71.2	69.6	66.7	63.8	61.1	58.4	55.9	53.5	49.2	45.4	52
54	90.0	88.4	86.6	85.0	83.3	81.6	80.0	78.3	76.7	75.0	73.5	72.1	70.5	67.6	64.9	62.1	59.6	57.1	54.8	50.6	46.8	54
56	90.0	88.4	86.8	85.4	83.6	82.0	80.5	78.9	77.4	75.7	74.4	72.9	71.3	68.6	65.9	63.3	60.8	58.4	56.1	51.9	48.2	56
58	90.0	88.5	87.0	85.5	84.0	82.5	81.0	79.5	78.0	76.6	75.2	73.8	72.4	69.6	67.0	64.5	62.1	59.8	57.5	53.4	49.7	58
60	90.0	88.6	87.1	85.7	84.3	82.9	81.5	80.1	78.7	77.3	76.0	74.6	73.3	70.7	68.2	65.8	63.4	61.2	59.0	55.0	51.3	60
62	90.0	88.7	87.3	86.0	84.6	83.3	82.0	80.7	79.4	78.0	76.8	75.5	74.3	71.8	69.4	67.1	64.9	62.7	60.6	56.7	53.1	62
64	90.0	88.7	87.5	86.2	85.0	83.8	82.5	81.3	80.0	78.8	77.6	76.4	75.3	72.9	70.7	68.5	66.3	64.3	62.3	58.5	55.0	64
66	90.0	88.8	87.7	86.5	85.3	84.2	83.0	81.9	80.8	79.6	78.5	77.4	76.3	74.1	72.0	69.9	67.9	65.9	64.0	60.3	56.9	66
68	90.0	88.9	87.9	86.8	85.7	84.6	83.6	82.5	81.5	80.4	79.4	78.4	77.3	75.3	73.3	71.4	69.5	67.6	65.8	62.3	59.1	68
Lat.	.00	.05	.10	.15	.20	.25	.30	.35	.40	.45	.50	.55	.60	.70	.80	.90	1.00	1.10	1.20	1.40	1.60	Lat.

TO NAME AZIMUTH

+	SOUTH in N. Latitudes / NORTH in S. Latitudes
−	NORTH in N. Latitudes / SOUTH in S. Latitudes

Hour Angle LESS than 180° = WEST

Hour Angle GREATER than 180° = EAST

Fig 69 Table C

114

18
WORKED EXAMPLES

1. To find Sun's GHA and declination for a certain time

Find the Sun's GHA and declination for 08 32 25 deck watch time, which was 2min 30sec slow of GMT on 5 May.

Deck watch time	08	32	25
Correction		+2	30
GMT	08	34	55

GHA for 0800	300°	49′.6
for 34min 55sec	8°	43′.8
Sun's GHA	309°	33′.4

Declination for 0800	16°	12′.7N
Interpolation for 0830	16°	13′.1N

2. To find the time the Sun will be on the meridian for noon latitude

On 21 May the noon EP of a vessel was 31° 25′ S, 165° 22′ W. Find the time of meridian passage.

Long to time 165°22′ =	11	01	28	
Time of transit	11	57	00	
Longtitude	11	01	28	W
GMT of Mer Pas	22	58	28	

Longitude west, Greenwich time best, so we add. Converting to ship's time if the vessel was 11 hours behind Greenwich, the Sun would be on the meridian at 11hr 58min 28sec.

3. To find the time of sunset and sunrise

A vessel is in EP 32° 36′ N, 15° 40′ W on October 20. Find the time of sunrise and sunset.

Time of Sunrise	06	33
Corr 32°N		−21
Sunrise	06	12
Time of Sunset	16	56
Corr 32°N		+21
Sunset	17	17

4. To find latitude by meridian altitude

On 3 May a vessel was in EP 29°41′S, 152°14′W. The lower limb of the Sun was observed when it was on the meridian. Index error −2.5; height of eye 8ft. If the sextant altitude was 44° 15′, find the latitude at noon.

Time of transit	11	57
Arc to time	10°	09′W
GMT of transit	22	06
Declination for 2200	15°	48′.2N
Observed altitude	44°	15′.0
Index error		− 2′.5
	44°	12′.5
Total correction		+ 12′.2
	44°	24′.7
	90°	00′
	45°	35′.3 (N)
Sun's declination*	15°	48′.2 N
Observed latitude	29°	47′.1 S

5. To convert local time to Greenwich time and vice versa

On 17 October a vessel was in EP 28° 14′ N, 20° 05′ W. If ship's time was 1015, what was GMT?

Converting arc into time

20° 05′ W	01	20	20
	10	15	00
GMT	11	35	20

On 26 October a vessel was in EP 39° 22′ N, 12° 56′ E. Deck watch time was 05hr 34min 21sec. Deck watch time was 3min 11sec fast of GMT.

Deck watch time	05	34	21
Correction		−3	11
GMT	05	31	10
Longtitude	00	51	44
Ship's time	06	22	54

6. Obtaining local hour angle (LHA)

You need to find LHA for all methods of working. On 24 May a vessel was in EP 39° 38′ N, 20° 05′ W. An observation of the Sun was made at 0845 ship's time, deck watch time 09hr 05min 35sec, which was 2min 10sec slow of Greenwich. Find the local hour angle.

	09	05	35
		+2	10
GMT	09	07	45

GHA sun for 0800	300°	48′.8
Corr 1hr 7min 45sec	16°	56′.3
	317°	45′.1
Longtitude	20°	05′.0 W
LHA	297°	40′.1

7. To find longitude using the Marq St Hilaire method

An observation of the Sun's lower limb was made on 10 October when the vessel was in EP 39° 25′ S, 32° 54′ E, at 0820 in time zone −2. Deck watch time was 06hr 12min 44sec, which was 3min 24sec slow of Greenwich. The sextant altitude was 34° 40′; index error 2.0′ on the arc; height of eye 3 metres. Find intercept, azimuth and position line to give assumed position (see Fig 70).

Deck watch time	06	12	44
Correction		+3	24
GMT	06	16	08

GHA for 0600	273°	13′.1	
GHA correction	4°	02′.0	
	277°	15′.1	
Longitude	32°	54′.0	E
Local hour angle	310°	09′.1	
Declination	6°	33′.5	S
Latitude	39°	25′.0	S
Lat diff. dec.	32°	51′.5	

To find intercept:

Log versine LHA	9.5505
Log cosine latitude	9.8879
Log cosine declination	9.9971
	9.4355

Natural versine	0.2725
+ lat difference declination	0.1600
Natural versine ZX	0.4325

Calculated ZD	55°	25′.5

Sextant altitude	34°	30′
Index error		−2′.0
	34°	28′.0
Total correction		11′.3
	34°	39′.3
	90°	00′.
Observed ZX	55°	20′.7
Calculated ZX	55°	25′.5
Intercept		4′.8

A = .700 +
B = .148 −
C = .552
Azimuth   = N 67° E
Dlong   = *Departure × secant latitude*
Dlong   = 5.2 × 1.3 (from table)
            = 6.8°E

Assumed position at 0820 = 39° 25′ S, 33° 01′ E

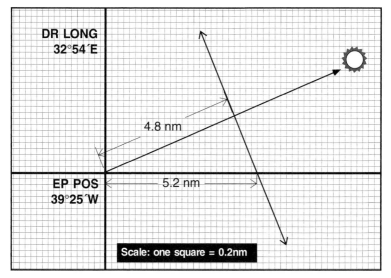

Fig 70 Worked example Plot 1

8. To find longitude using sight reduction tables and chosen longitude
Using the same information as in example 7

GHA for 0600	273°	13´.1	
Correction	4°	02´.0	
	277°	15´.1	
Chosen long	32°	44´.9	E
LHA	310°	00´.0	

For lat 39°	Hc	34°	14´
d corr +42			+23´
Corr Hc		34°	37´

Calculated alt	34°	37´
Observed alt	34°	39´.3
Intercept		02.3 (T)
Z = 067°		

	33°	00´.0
Chosen long	32°	44´.9E
		15´.1

119

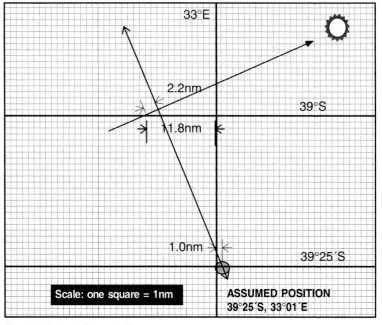

Fig 72 Worked Example Plot 2

Dlong = *Dep* × *Sec lat*
        = 13 × 1.29
        = 16.8

9. A Sun-run position

On 31 October a vessel was in EP 39° 06′ N, 6° 25′ E, heading towards Minorca. At 0845 an observation of the lower limb of the Sun gave a sextant altitude of 23° 01′. The deck watch time was 08hr 27min 32sec, which was 2min 10sec fast of Greenwich. Height of eye 2 metres; index error 2′.5 off the arc. A sextant altitude of the Sun was taken when it was on the meridian, which gave an altitude of 64° 38′. Between the sights the vessel was steering 282°(T) at 5 knots. Find the vessel's observed position at noon.

1 To find GMT and local hour angle (LHA)

Deck watch time	08	27	32
Error		–2	10
GMT	08	25	22

GHA for 0800	304°	05′.2	
Correction	6°	20′.5	
Corrected GHA	310°	25′.7	
Longitude	6°	25′.0	E
Local hour angle (LHA)	316°	50′.7	
Declination	14°	04′.0	S
Latitude	39°	06′.0	N
Lat diff dec	53°	10′.0	

2 To find intercept

Log versine LHA	9.4322
Log cosine latitude	9.8899
Log cosine declination	9.9868
	9.3089
Change to natural versine	0.2036
Nat/vers/lat/diff/decl.	0.4005
	0.6041
Calculated ZX	66° 40′

3 To find observed zenith distance and intercept

Sextant altitude	23°	01′
Index error		+ 2′.5
	23°	03′.5
Total correction		11′.2
	23°	14′.7
	90°	00′
Observed zenith distance	66°	45′.3
Calculated zenith distance	66°	40′
Intercept		5.3 (A)

4 To find azimuth, or bearing

A	=	.870 +
B	=	.366 +
C	=	1.236 +
Az	=	S 47°E

To find Dlong

Dlong = departure × secant latitude

Dlong = 7 × 1.29

= 9.03

Assumed position at 0845 39° 06′ N, 06° 16′ E

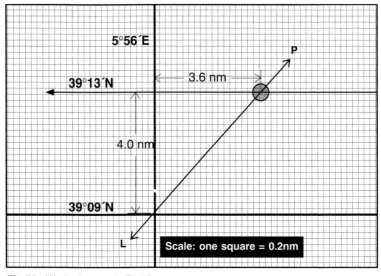

5°56′E

39°13′N

3.6 nm

P

4.0 nm

39°09′N

L

Scale: one square = 0.2nm

Fig 72 Worked example Plot 3

5 To find noon DR position (see Fig 74)

Vessel steered 282°(T) at 5 knots

Position at 0845	39°	06′.0	N
		+ 3′.5	N
DR position at noon	39°	9′.5	N
Position at 0845	6°	16′.0	E
		−20′.2	W
DR position at noon	5°	55′.8	E

Dlong = departure × secant latitude

Dlong = 15.7 × 1.29

= 20.25

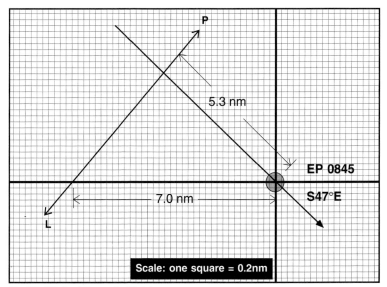

Fig 73 Worked Example Plot 4

6 To find latitude at noon

Time sun on meridian	11hr	44min	
Transit 1200			
Longitude	23°	40′. E	
GMT	12hr 07min 00sec		
Sextant altitude	64°	38′	
Index error		+2′.5	
	64°	40′.5	
Total correction		13′.0	
	64°	53′.5	
	90°	00′.0	
	25°	06′.5	
Declination	14°	06′.5	S
Latitude	39°	13′.0	N

As vessel is north of DR the transferred position line shows the vessel to be east of the noon DR by departure of 2 miles.

$$Dlong = dep \times sec\ lat$$
$$= 2 \times 1.29$$
$$= 2.58$$

Observed noon position = 39° 12′.0N, 5° 58′.4E

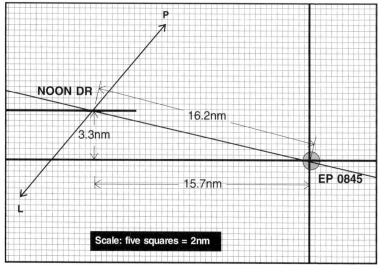

Fig 71 Worked example Plot 5

10. To find latitude by Polaris

A vessel was in EP 38° 55′ N, 15° 07′W, on 4 May. An observation was made of Polaris during evening twilight. What was the observed latitude? Deck watch time was 19hr 25min 42sec, which was 1min 50sec slow of GMT. Sextant altitude 38° 50′. Index error 3′.2 on the arc; height of eye 3 metres.

To find LHA Aries		
GHA for 1800	132°	21′.6
Correction	21°	56′.6
	154°	18′.2
Longtitude	15°	07′.0 W
LHA Aries	139°	11′.2
From Pole Star table, correction to altitude		
Sex alt	38°	50′.0
IE		– 3′.2
	38°	46′.8
Correction		– 4′.2
Latitude	38°	42′.6 N
Pole Star correction		11′.4
	38°	54′.0 N

11. To find position using stars and sight reduction tables

On 11 May a vessel was in DR position 39° 06′ N, 35° 14′ W.
During evening twilight the following stars were observed:
Capella   sextant altitude 52° 26′   DWT 19 43 21
Kochab   sextant altitude 36° 28′   DWT 19 44 30
Sirius   sextant altitude 28° 10′   DWT 19 45 15
Regulus   sextant altitude 57° 13′   DWT 19 46 22
Index error 2.5 off the arc;   Height of eye 3 metres
Find the vessel's observed position. Deck watch time was 2min
20sec slow of GMT.

	CAPELLA	KOCHAB	SIRIUS	REGULUS
Deck watch	19 43 21	19 44 30	19 45 15	19 46 22
Error	+2 20	+2 20	+2 20	+2 20
GMT	19 45 41	19 46 50	19 47 35	19 48 42
GHA Aries	139° 15′.6	139° 15′.6	139° 15′.6	139° 15′.6
GHA corr	26° 29′.6	26° 46′.9	26° 58′.2	27° 15′.0
GHA Aries	165° 45′.2	166° 02′.5	166° 13′.8	166° 30′.6
Chosen long	35° 45′.2	36° 02′.5	36° 13′.8	36° 30′.6
LHA Aries	130°	130°	130°	130°
Hc	52° 24′	36° 33′	28°07′	56° 43′.0
Az (Zn)	298°	020°	212°	138°
Sex alt	52° 24′	36° 28′.0	28° 10′.0	57° 13′
I E	+2′.5	+2′.5	+2′.5	+2′.5
	52° 28′.5	36° 30′.5	28° 12′.5	57° 15′.5
Alt corr	–3′.7	–4′.4	–5′.0	–3′.7
Obs alt	52° 28′.8	36° 26′.1	28° 07′.5	57° 11′.8
Hc	52° 24′	36° 33′.0	28° 07′	56° 43′.0
Intercept	0.8 T	6.9 A	0.5T	28.8 T

In the diagram (Fig 75), the minutes of the chosen longitude have to
be converted into miles for departure for each star for plotting:

Capella: chosen longitude 35° 45′.2 W

The meridian drawn is 36°W, so Capella's chosen longitude lies to
the east of 36°W, so 14′.8min of longitude have to be converted to
departure.

Departure = Dlong × cos lat

125

$$= 14.8 \times 0.78$$
$$= 11.5 \text{ for Capella}$$

Kochab: chosen longitude 36° 02.5′ W
$$= 2.5 \times 0.78$$
$$= 1.95$$

Sirius: chosen longitude 36° 13′.8 W
$$= 18.8 \times 0.78$$
$$= 10.7$$

Regulus: chosen longitude 36° 30′.6
$$= 30.6 \times 0.78$$
$$= 23.9$$

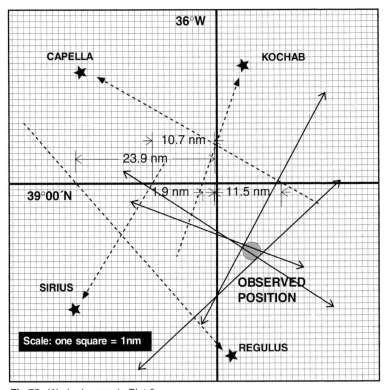

Fig 75 Worked example Plot 6

These distances for each star are measured from the vertical 36°W in an east-west direction, at which point the bearing of the star is laid off. The intercept is then plotted along the bearing by the amount shown, and the position line is drawn at right angles to the bearing at that point.

The position found in the diagram or plot shows the vessel to the south and east of the DR position. Using a ruler, the vessel is about 11 miles south and has a departure of 7 miles which has to be converted back to Dlong.

Dlong = dep × sec lat
= 7 × 1.29
= 9.03 min of longitude east.

	39°	00′ N		36°	00′ W
		11′ S			9′ E
Observed position =	38°	49′ N		35°	51′ W

12. To find a position line from the Moon (using sight reduction tables)

An observation was made of the Moon's lower limb when in DR position 38° 56′ N, 14° 20′ E during the morning of 9 October. Find the intercept and azimuth and draw the position line. Height of eye 2 metres; index error 4′.2 on the arc; deck watch time 07hr 30min 22sec, which was correct with Greenwich. The sextant altitude of the lower limb of the Moon was 34° 51′; vessel was in Z–1.

1 Find GHA

[Variation per hour	14°	22′]	
GHA for 0600	27°	55′.2	
For 0700hr	+14°	22′.0	
For 30min	7°	11′.0	
For 22sec		+5′.3	
GHA	49°	33′.5	
Longitude(chosen)	14°	26′.5	E
LHA	64°	00′.0	
[Declination	26°	35′.5 N]	

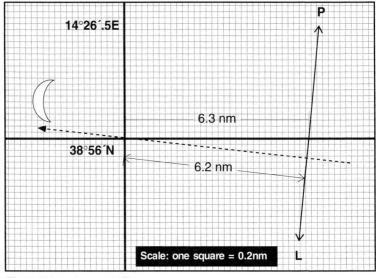

Fig 76 Worked example Plot 7

2 To find intercept from air tables

Hc = 35° 36′   d = +30′   Z = 84°

Az = 360° − Z = 276°

Correction from declination correction table = 18′

	35°	36′
		+18′
Tabulated altitude	35°	54′
Sextant altitude	34°	51′.0
Index error		−4′.2
	34°	46′.8
Total correction		53′.8

[Horizontal parallax 59.6]

Height of eye correction		
		7′.2
Observed alt	35°	47′.8
Tabulated alt	35°	54′.0
Intercept		6.2 (A)

Converting departure into Dlong

Dlong = Dep × sec lat

    =   7.0 × 1.29

    =   9.0

Assumed position 38° 56′.0 N, 14° 35′.5 E

13. Planet sight reduction

A vessel was in DR position 39° 02′ S, 42° 35′ W, on 10 May. At evening twilight an observation was made of Jupiter. Deck watch time was 22hr 35min 12sec, which was 4sec slow of GMT; index error +2′.0; height of eye 3 metres. If the sextant altitude was 18° 31′, find the assumed position, intercept and azimuth.

1 To find GMT and local hour angle (LHA)

Deck watch	22	35	12	
Error			+4	
GMT	22	35	16	
GHA for 10 May		128°	15′.1	
Correction		8°	46′.2	
			4′.0	
Corrected GHA		137°	05′.3	
Longitude (chosen)		42°	05′.3	W
Local hour angle (LHA)		95°	00′	

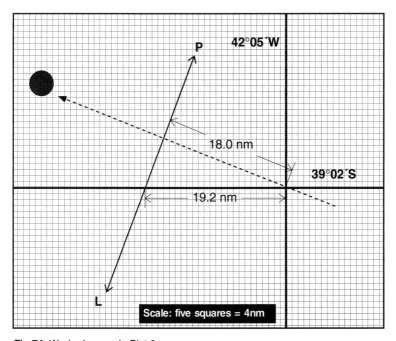

Fig 74 Worked example Plot 8

2 Declination for Jupiter   23°   18′.2 N (no correction)

3 To find tabulated altitude and azimuth
  Hc = 10°35′   d = +37′   Z = 069°
  Az = 360° − Z = 291°

4 To find intercept

Sextant altitude	10°	59′.0
Index error		+2′.0
	11°	01′.0
Total correction		−8′.0
Observed alt	10°	53′.0
Tabulated alt	10°	35′.0
Intercept		18 (T)

5. Plot azimuth and position line

  Dlong = *Dep* × *sec lat*
       =   22 × 1.29
       =   28.4
  Assumed position 39° 00′.0S, 42° 33′.4 W

19

EXERCISES

1 Converting Sextant Altitude to True Altitude

(a) On 1 October a sextant altitude of the Sun's lower limb was 43° 24′. Index error 2′.0 on the arc; height of eye 3 metres. What was the true altitude?

(b) On 10 May a sextant altitude of Sirius was 62° 15′. Index error 3′.5 off the arc; height of eye 2 metres. What was the true altitude?

(c) On 21 May a sextant altitude of Venus was 34° 55′. Index error 1′.5 on the arc; height of eye 4 metres. What was the true altitude?

2 Time the Sun is on the Meridian

(a) A vessel is in DR position 39°50′N, 7°22′W, on 6 May. What time will the Sun be on the meridian? The vessel is in time zone Z+1.

(b) A vessel is in DR position 39°05′S, 154°15′W, on 2 October. What time will the Sun be on the meridian? The vessel is in time zone Z+10.

(c) On 12 May a vessel is in DR position 38°52′N, 10°15′E. What time will the Sun be on the meridian. Time zone Z −1.

3 Times of Sunset and Sunrise

(a) What will be the time of sunset on 10 May in latitude 39°S?

(b) What will be the time of sunrise on 15 October in latitude 50°N?

(c) What will be the time of twilight on 2 May in latitude
15°S?

4 Sun Meridian Altitude Reduction

(a) On 12 October, when in DR position 39° 04′ N, 18° 20′ W,
the lower limb of the Sun was observed on the meridian. If
the sextant altitude was 43° 10′ bearing south, index error
2′.2 off the arc and the height of eye was 2 metres, what
was the observed latitude?

(b) On 7 May, while in DR position 38° 45′ S, 142° 22′ E, the
lower limb of the Sun was observed on the meridian. If the
sextant altitude waas 34° 24′ bearing north, index error 4′.0
on the arc, height of eye 2.5 metres, what was the observed
latitude?

(c) At noon on 26 May a vessel was in DR position 39° 15′ N,
8° 06′ E, when the lower limb of the Sun was observed on
the meridian. If the sextant altitude was 71° 34′ bearing
south, index error 2.5 off the arc, height of eye 3 metres,
what was the observed latitude?

5 Sun Sight Reductions

(a) On 2 May a vessel was in DR position 39° 06′ N, 31° 22′ W.
An observation was made of the Sun's lower limb at 0820
(time zone Z+2). The deck watch time was 10hr 25min
28sec, which was correct with GMT. The sextant altitude
was 37° 04′, index error 2′.0 off the arc, height of eye
3 metres. What was the assumed position at 0820, the intercept and azimuth?

(b) On 10 October a vessel is in EP 38° 42′ S, 158° 24′ E,
when an observation of the Sun's lower limb was made at
0815. The time zone was Z–10 and deck watch time was
21hr 41min 56sec, which was 10sec slow on GMT. The
sextant altitude was 32° 20′. The index error was 2′.1 and
height of eye 2.4 metres. Find the assumed position, intercept and azimuth.

(c) On 23 May a vessel was in DR position 39° 02′ N, 18° 05′ E,
when an observation was made of the Sun's lower limb at

0810. Time zone Z–1; deck watch time 06hr 55min 21sec, which was 5sec fast of GMT. If the sextant altitude was 37° 55′, index error +1′.5 and height of eye 2.4 metres, what was the assumed position, intercept and azimuth?

6 Sun Run Reductions

(a) On 17 October a vessel was in DR position 39° 02′ S, 138° 20′E, heading towards Melbourne. An observation of the Sun's lower limb was made at 0830 and again at noon, when it was on the meridian. At 0830 the sextant altitude was 36°04′. Index error was –2′.0, height of eye 3 metres. Deck watch time was 23hr 16min 40sec, which was 4sec slow of GMT. The log read 186. Between 0830 and noon the vessel steered 065°(T) and at noon the log read 211. A sextant meridian altitude of the Sun was 68°04′. Find the vessel's observed noon position.

(b) On 3 October a vessel was in EP 39° 08′ N, 23° 16′ W, approaching the Azores, at noon. The morning was overcast, so a morning sunsight was not possible. The sextant meridian altitude at noon was 46° 38′. Index error was +3′.5; height of eye 2.4 metres; log set to zero. At 1540 an observation was made of the Sun's lower limb. Since noon the vessel had steered 245°(T) and the log read 21. The sextant altitude was 20° 50′. Deck watch time was 17hr 13min 08sec, which was 8sec fast of GMT. Find the vessel's position at 1540.

(c) On 22 May a vessel was in DR position 38°57′N, 61°20′W, approaching Bermuda. At 0815 an observation was made of the Sun's lower limb. Index error was +1′.5; height of eye 3 metres. Sextant altitude was 39°15′; deck watch time was 12hr 21min 42sec, which was 32sec fast of GMT; the time zone was Z+4 and the log read 185.
From 0815 until noon the vessel steered 215°(T), and at noon the log read 212. The sextant meridian altitude was 71°37′ of the Sun's lower limb. Find the position of the vessel at noon.

7 Latitude by Polaris

(a) A vessel was in DR position 39° 10′ N, 15° 05′ W, on 28 May. An observation was made of Polaris during evening twilight. The deck watch time was 21hr 07min 47sec, which was 45sec slow of GMT. Index error was 2′.0 off the arc; height of eye was 10ft; sextant altitude 38° 35′. Find the latitude.

(b) A vessel was in DR position 38° 47′ N, 145° 52′ W, on 14 October. An observation was made of Polaris during morning twilight. The deck watch time was 15hr 25min 10sec, which was correct with GMT. The vessel was in Z +10; index error –3′.5; height of eye 3 metres. If the sextant altitude was 39° 40′, what was the observed latitude?

(c) A vessel was in EP 39° 08′ N, 7° 34′ E on the 17th day. An observation was made of Polaris during evening twilight. The deck watch time was 19hr 21min 32sec and was 6sec slow of GMT. Index error was –1.5; height of eye 2.4 metres. If the sextant altitude was 38° 40′, find the observed latitude.

8 Star Sight Reductions

(a) On 3 May a vessel was in EP 39° 02′ N, 20° 42′ W, and during evening twilight observed the following stars. Plot the vessel's position.

Star	Deck watch time	Sextant altitude	
Capella	20 28 14	40°	42′
Arcturus	20 29 36	30°	48′
Sirius	20 30 42	19°	00′
Regulus	20 32 07	62°	51′

The deck watch was 15min slow of GMT: index error was +3′.0; height of eye 3 metres.

(b) On 5 October a vessel was in DR position 39° 08′ S, 171° 22′ W, and during morning twilight observed the following stars:

Procyon	16 55 11	42°	37′
Acrux	16 56 31	34°	59′
Achenar	16 57 40	40°	49′
Betelguese	16 59 05	42°	28′

Deck watch time was 2min 23sec slow of GMT; index error +2′.5; height of eye 3 metres. Plot the vessel's position.

(c) On 21 May a vessel was in EP 39° 05′ N, 13° 42′ E, and during morning twilight observed the following:

Venus	03 07 22	11°	56′
Altair	03 09 15	60°	03′
Alpheratz	03 10 30	38°	13′
Kochab	03 11 42	40°	41′

Plot the vessel's position. The deck watch was 12 sec fast of GMT; index error was 2′.0 on the arc; height of eye was 3 metres.

20
ANSWERS

Chapter 6

2   15 32 44 GMT
3   11 31 48 GMT
4   19 39 12 GMT
5   01 38 04 GMT

Latitudes

2   Time of meridian passage 14hr 07min 04sec GMT; observed latitude 12° 20′.7 N
3   Time of meridian passage 23hr 50min 52sec GMT; observed latitude 35° 17′.0 S

Exercises

1a   43° 34′
1b   62° 15′.5
1c   34° 49′.0

2a   12hr 26min 28sec GMT
2b   22hr 06min GMT
2c   11hr 15min GMT

3a   1909
3b   0621
3c   0615

4a   Latitude 39° 10′ N
4b   Latitude 38° 45′.7 S
4c   Latitude 39° 18′.5 N

5a	39° 06′ N, 31° 19′ W; intercept 2T; azimuth 101°
5b	38° 42′ S, 158° 33′ E; intercept 14T; azimuth 110°
5c	39° 02′ N, 18° 15′.5 E; intercept 3.5; azimuth 094°
6a	38° 53′ S, 138° 39′ E
6b	38° 75′.5 N, 23° 18′ W; intercept 19.5 T; azimuth 24°.4
6c	38° 34′.5 N, 61° 40′ W; intercept at 0815, 6.5A; azimuth 095°
7a	35° 15′.6 N
7b	38° 45′.2 N
7c	38° 40′.3 N
8a	39° 04′ N, 20° 38′ W
8b	39° 28′ S, 171° 17′ W
8c	38° 58′ N, 13° 36′ E

APPENDIX
NAVIGATION TABLES

3:36   ⊙   SUN — May, 1990 — ARIES   ♈

Tuesday, 1st May

G.M.T. h	SUN G.H.A.	SUN Dec.	ARIES G.H.A.	G.M.T. h
00	180 42.7	N14 55.9	218 39.9	00
02	210 42.8	14 57.5	248 44.8	02
04	240 43.0	14 59.0	278 49.7	04
06	270 43.1	15 00.5	308 54.7	06
08	300 43.3	15 02.0	338 59.6	08
10	330 43.4	15 03.5	9 04.5	10
12	0 43.6	15 05.0	39 09.4	12
14	30 43.7	15 06.6	69 14.4	14
16	60 43.9	15 08.1	99 19.3	16
18	90 44.0	15 09.6	129 24.2	18
20	120 44.2	15 11.1	159 29.2	20
22	150 44.3	N15 12.6	189 34.1	22

Wednesday, 2nd May

G.M.T. h	SUN G.H.A.	SUN Dec.	ARIES G.H.A.	G.M.T. h
00	180 44.5	N15 14.1	219 39.0	00
02	210 44.6	15 15.6	249 43.9	02
04	240 44.8	15 17.1	279 48.9	04
06	270 44.9	15 18.6	309 53.8	06
08	300 45.1	15 20.1	339 58.7	08
10	330 45.2	15 21.6	10 03.7	10
12	0 45.4	15 23.1	40 08.6	12
14	30 45.5	15 24.6	70 13.5	14
16	60 45.6	15 26.0	100 18.4	16
18	90 45.8	15 27.5	130 23.4	18
20	120 45.9	15 29.0	160 28.3	20
22	150 46.0	N15 30.5	190 33.2	22

Thursday, 3rd May

G.M.T. h	SUN G.H.A.	SUN Dec.	ARIES G.H.A.	G.M.T. h
00	180 46.2	N15 32.0	220 38.2	00
02	210 46.3	15 33.5	250 43.1	02
04	240 46.4	15 34.9	280 48.0	04
06	270 46.6	15 36.4	310 52.9	06
08	300 46.7	15 37.9	340 57.9	08
10	330 46.8	15 39.4	11 02.8	10
12	0 47.0	15 40.8	41 07.7	12
14	30 47.1	15 42.3	71 12.6	14
16	60 47.2	15 43.8	101 17.6	16
18	90 47.4	15 45.2	131 22.5	18
20	120 47.5	15 46.7	161 27.4	20
22	150 47.6	N15 48.2	191 32.4	22

Friday, 4th May

G.M.T. h	SUN G.H.A.	SUN Dec.	ARIES G.H.A.	G.M.T. h
00	180 47.7	N15 49.6	221 37.3	00
02	210 47.9	15 51.1	251 42.2	02
04	240 48.0	15 52.5	281 47.1	04
06	270 48.1	15 54.0	311 52.1	06
08	300 48.2	15 55.4	341 57.0	08
10	330 48.3	15 56.9	12 01.9	10
12	0 48.5	15 58.3	42 06.9	12
14	30 48.6	15 59.8	72 11.8	14
16	60 48.7	16 01.2	102 16.7	16
18	90 48.8	16 02.7	132 21.6	18
20	120 48.9	16 04.1	162 26.6	20
22	150 49.0	N16 05.6	192 31.5	22

Saturday, 5th May

G.M.T. h	SUN G.H.A.	SUN Dec.	ARIES G.H.A.	G.M.T. h
00	180 49.2	N16 07.0	222 36.4	00
02	210 49.3	16 08.4	252 41.4	02
04	240 49.4	16 09.9	282 46.3	04
06	270 49.5	16 11.3	312 51.2	06
08	300 49.6	16 12.7	342 56.1	08
10	330 49.7	16 14.2	13 01.1	10
12	0 49.8	16 15.6	43 06.0	12
14	30 49.9	16 17.0	73 10.9	14
16	60 50.0	16 18.4	103 15.9	16
18	90 50.1	16 19.9	133 20.8	18
20	120 50.2	16 21.3	163 25.7	20
22	150 50.3	N16 22.7	193 30.6	22

Sunday, 6th May

G.M.T. h	SUN G.H.A.	SUN Dec.	ARIES G.H.A.	G.M.T. h
00	180 50.4	N16 24.1	223 35.6	00
02	210 50.5	16 25.5	253 40.5	02
04	240 50.6	16 26.9	283 45.4	04
06	270 50.7	16 28.3	313 50.4	06
08	300 50.8	16 29.8	343 55.3	08
10	330 50.9	16 31.2	14 00.2	10
12	0 51.0	16 32.6	44 05.1	12
14	30 51.1	16 34.0	74 10.1	14
16	60 51.2	16 35.4	104 15.0	16
18	90 51.3	16 36.8	134 19.9	18
20	120 51.4	16 38.2	164 24.9	20
22	150 51.5	N16 39.6	194 29.8	22

Monday, 7th May

G.M.T. h	SUN G.H.A.	SUN Dec.	ARIES G.H.A.	G.M.T. h
00	180 51.6	N16 40.9	224 34.7	00
02	210 51.7	16 42.3	254 39.6	02
04	240 51.8	16 43.7	284 44.6	04
06	270 51.9	16 45.1	314 49.5	06
08	300 51.9	16 46.5	344 54.4	08
10	330 52.0	16 47.9	14 59.3	10
12	0 52.1	16 49.3	45 04.3	12
14	30 52.2	16 50.6	75 09.2	14
16	60 52.3	16 52.0	105 14.1	16
18	90 52.4	16 53.4	135 19.1	18
20	120 52.4	16 54.8	165 24.0	20
22	150 52.5	N16 56.1	195 28.9	22

Tuesday, 8th May

G.M.T. h	SUN G.H.A.	SUN Dec.	ARIES G.H.A.	G.M.T. h
00	180 52.6	N16 57.5	225 33.8	00
02	210 52.7	16 58.9	255 38.8	02
04	240 52.8	17 00.2	285 43.7	04
06	270 52.8	17 01.6	315 48.6	06
08	300 52.9	17 03.0	345 53.6	08
10	330 53.0	17 04.3	15 58.5	10
12	0 53.0	17 05.7	46 03.4	12
14	30 53.1	17 07.0	76 08.3	14
16	60 53.2	17 08.4	106 13.3	16
18	90 53.3	17 09.7	136 18.2	18
20	120 53.3	17 11.1	166 23.1	20
22	150 53.4	N17 12.4	196 28.1	22

Wednesday, 9th May

G.M.T. h	SUN G.H.A.	SUN Dec.	ARIES G.H.A.	G.M.T. h
00	180 53.5	N17 13.8	226 33.0	00
02	210 53.5	17 15.1	256 37.9	02
04	240 53.6	17 16.5	286 42.9	04
06	270 53.7	17 17.8	316 47.8	06
08	300 53.7	17 19.1	346 52.7	08
10	330 53.8	17 20.5	16 57.6	10
12	0 53.8	17 21.8	47 02.6	12
14	30 53.9	17 23.1	77 07.5	14
16	60 54.0	17 24.5	107 12.4	16
18	90 54.0	17 25.8	137 17.3	18
20	120 54.1	17 27.1	167 22.3	20
22	150 54.1	N17 28.4	197 27.2	22

Thursday, 10th May

G.M.T. h	SUN G.H.A.	SUN Dec.	ARIES G.H.A.	G.M.T. h
00	180 54.2	N17 29.8	227 32.1	00
02	210 54.2	17 31.1	257 37.1	02
04	240 54.3	17 32.4	287 42.0	04
06	270 54.3	17 33.7	317 46.9	06
08	300 54.4	17 35.0	347 51.8	08
10	330 54.4	17 36.3	17 56.8	10
12	0 54.5	17 37.7	48 01.7	12
14	30 54.5	17 39.0	78 06.6	14
16	60 54.6	17 40.3	108 11.6	16
18	90 54.6	17 41.6	138 16.5	18
20	120 54.7	17 42.9	168 21.4	20
22	150 54.7	N17 44.2	198 26.3	22

Friday, 11th May

G.M.T. h	SUN G.H.A.	SUN Dec.	ARIES G.H.A.	G.M.T. h
00	180 54.8	N17 45.5	228 31.3	00
02	210 54.8	17 46.8	258 36.2	02
04	240 54.9	17 48.0	288 41.1	04
06	270 54.9	17 49.3	318 46.0	06
08	300 54.9	17 50.6	348 51.0	08
10	330 55.0	17 51.9	18 55.9	10
12	0 55.0	17 53.2	49 00.8	12
14	30 55.0	17 54.5	79 05.8	14
16	60 55.1	17 55.8	109 10.7	16
18	90 55.1	17 57.0	139 15.6	18
20	120 55.1	17 58.3	169 20.5	20
22	150 55.2	N17 59.6	199 25.5	22

Saturday, 12th May

G.M.T. h	SUN G.H.A.	SUN Dec.	ARIES G.H.A.	G.M.T. h
00	180 55.2	N18 00.9	229 30.4	00
02	210 55.2	18 02.1	259 35.3	02
04	240 55.3	18 03.4	289 40.3	04
06	270 55.3	18 04.7	319 45.2	06
08	300 55.3	18 05.9	349 50.1	08
10	330 55.3	18 07.2	19 55.0	10
12	0 55.4	18 06.4	50 00.0	12
14	30 55.4	18 08.7	80 04.8	14
16	60 55.4	18 11.0	110 09.8	16
18	90 55.4	18 12.2	140 14.8	18
20	120 55.5	18 13.5	170 19.7	20
22	150 55.5	N18 14.7	200 24.6	22

Sunday, 13th May

G.M.T. h	SUN G.H.A.	SUN Dec.	ARIES G.H.A.	G.M.T. h
00	180 55.5	N18 16.0	230 29.5	00
02	210 55.5	18 17.2	260 34.5	02
04	240 55.5	18 18.4	290 39.4	04
06	270 55.5	18 19.7	320 44.3	06
08	300 55.5	18 20.9	350 49.3	08
10	330 55.6	18 22.2	20 54.2	10
12	0 55.6	18 23.4	50 59.1	12
14	30 55.6	18 24.6	81 04.0	14
16	60 55.6	18 25.8	111 09.0	16
18	90 55.6	18 27.1	141 13.9	18
20	120 55.6	18 28.3	171 18.8	20
22	150 55.6	N18 29.5	201 23.8	22

Monday, 14th May

G.M.T. h	SUN G.H.A.	SUN Dec.	ARIES G.H.A.	G.M.T. h
00	180 55.6	N18 30.7	231 28.7	00
02	210 55.7	18 32.0	261 33.6	02
04	240 55.7	18 33.2	291 38.5	04
06	270 55.7	18 34.4	321 43.5	06
08	300 55.7	18 35.6	351 48.4	08
10	330 55.7	18 36.8	21 53.3	10
12	0 55.7	18 38.0	51 58.2	12
14	30 55.7	18 39.2	82 03.2	14
16	60 55.7	18 40.4	112 08.1	16
18	90 55.7	18 41.6	142 13.0	18
20	120 55.7	18 42.8	172 18.0	20
22	150 55.7	N18 44.0	202 22.9	22

Tuesday, 15th May

G.M.T. h	SUN G.H.A.	SUN Dec.	ARIES G.H.A.	G.M.T. h
00	180 55.6	N18 45.2	232 27.8	00
02	210 55.6	18 46.4	262 32.7	02
04	240 55.6	18 47.6	292 37.7	04
06	270 55.6	18 48.8	322 42.6	06
08	300 55.6	18 50.0	352 47.5	08
10	330 55.6	18 51.2	22 52.5	10
12	0 55.6	18 52.3	52 57.4	12
14	30 55.6	18 53.5	83 02.3	14
16	60 55.6	18 54.7	113 07.2	16
18	90 55.5	18 55.9	143 12.2	18
20	120 55.5	18 57.0	173 17.1	20
22	150 55.5	N18 58.2	203 22.0	22

To interpolate SUN G.H.A. see page 4:7   To interpolate ARIES G.H.A. see page 4:8

⊙ **SUN — May, 1990 — ARIES** ♈ **3:37**

G.M.T.	SUN G.H.A.	Dec.	ARIES G.H.A.	G.M.T.

Wednesday, 16th May

h	SUN G.H.A.	Dec.	ARIES G.H.A.	h
00	180 55.5	N18 59.4	233 27.0	00
02	210 55.5	19 00.5	263 31.9	02
04	240 55.5	19 01.7	293 36.8	04
06	270 55.4	19 02.9	323 41.7	06
08	300 55.4	19 04.0	353 46.7	08
10	330 55.4	19 05.2	23 51.6	10
12	0 55.4	19 06.3	53 56.5	12
14	30 55.3	19 07.5	84 01.5	14
16	60 55.3	19 08.6	114 06.4	16
18	90 55.3	19 09.8	144 11.3	18
20	120 55.3	19 10.9	174 16.2	20
22	150 55.2	N19 12.1	204 21.2	22

Monday, 21st May

h	SUN G.H.A.	Dec.	ARIES G.H.A.	h
00	180 52.6	N20 05.3	238 22.7	00
02	210 52.5	20 06.3	268 27.6	02
04	240 52.5	20 07.3	298 32.5	04
06	270 52.4	20 08.3	328 37.4	06
08	300 52.3	20 09.4	358 42.4	08
10	330 52.2	20 10.4	28 47.3	10
12	0 52.1	20 11.4	58 52.2	12
14	30 52.1	20 12.4	88 57.1	14
16	60 52.0	20 13.4	119 02.1	16
18	90 51.9	20 14.4	149 07.0	18
20	120 51.8	20 15.4	179 11.9	20
22	150 51.7	N20 16.4	209 16.9	22

Saturday, 26th May

h	SUN G.H.A.	Dec.	ARIES G.H.A.	h
00	180 46.3	N21 02.0	243 18.3	00
02	210 46.2	21 03.5	273 23.3	02
04	240 46.0	21 04.4	303 28.2	04
06	270 45.9	21 05.2	333 33.1	06
08	300 45.8	21 06.1	3 38.1	08
10	330 45.6	21 07.0	33 43.0	10
12	0 45.5	21 07.8	63 47.9	12
14	30 45.4	21 08.7	93 52.8	14
16	60 45.2	21 09.6	123 57.8	16
18	90 45.1	21 10.4	154 02.7	18
20	120 45.0	21 11.3	184 07.6	20
22	150 44.8	N21 12.1	214 12.6	22

Thursday, 17th May

h	SUN G.H.A.	Dec.	ARIES G.H.A.	h
00	180 55.2	N19 13.2	234 26.1	00
02	210 55.2	19 14.4	264 31.0	02
04	240 55.1	19 15.5	294 36.0	04
06	270 55.1	19 16.6	324 40.9	06
08	300 55.1	19 17.8	354 45.8	08
10	330 55.0	19 18.9	24 50.7	10
12	0 55.0	19 20.0	54 55.7	12
14	30 55.0	19 21.1	85 00.6	14
16	60 54.9	19 22.3	115 05.5	16
18	90 54.9	19 23.4	145 10.5	18
20	120 54.9	19 24.5	175 15.4	20
22	150 54.8	N19 25.6	205 20.3	22

Tuesday, 22nd May

h	SUN G.H.A.	Dec.	ARIES G.H.A.	h
00	180 51.6	N20 17.4	239 21.8	00
02	210 51.5	20 18.4	269 26.7	02
04	240 51.4	20 19.4	299 31.6	04
06	270 51.3	20 20.4	329 36.6	06
08	300 51.3	20 21.4	359 41.5	08
10	330 51.2	20 22.4	29 46.4	10
12	0 51.1	20 23.4	59 51.4	12
14	30 50.9	20 24.4	89 56.3	14
16	60 50.9	20 25.4	120 01.2	16
18	90 50.8	20 26.3	150 06.1	18
20	120 50.7	20 27.3	180 11.1	20
22	150 50.6	N20 28.3	210 16.0	22

Sunday, 27th May

h	SUN G.H.A.	Dec.	ARIES G.H.A.	h
00	180 44.7	N21 13.0	244 17.5	00
02	210 44.5	21 13.8	274 22.4	02
04	240 44.4	21 14.7	304 27.3	04
06	270 44.2	21 15.5	334 32.3	06
08	300 44.1	21 16.4	4 37.2	08
10	330 44.0	21 17.2	34 42.1	10
12	0 43.8	21 18.1	64 47.1	12
14	30 43.7	21 18.9	94 52.0	14
16	60 43.5	21 19.7	124 56.9	16
18	90 43.4	21 20.5	155 01.8	18
20	120 43.2	21 21.4	185 06.8	20
22	150 43.1	N21 22.2	215 11.7	22

Friday, 18th May

h	SUN G.H.A.	Dec.	ARIES G.H.A.	h
00	180 54.8	N19 26.7	235 25.2	00
02	210 54.7	19 27.8	265 30.2	02
04	240 54.7	19 28.9	295 35.1	04
06	270 54.6	19 30.1	325 40.0	06
08	300 54.6	19 31.2	355 44.9	08
10	330 54.6	19 32.3	25 49.9	10
12	0 54.5	19 33.4	55 54.8	12
14	30 54.5	19 34.5	85 59.7	14
16	60 54.4	19 35.6	116 04.7	16
18	90 54.4	19 36.6	146 09.6	18
20	120 54.3	19 37.7	176 14.5	20
22	150 54.3	N19 38.8	206 19.4	22

Wednesday, 23rd May

h	SUN G.H.A.	Dec.	ARIES G.H.A.	h
00	180 50.5	N20 29.3	240 20.9	00
02	210 50.4	20 30.2	270 25.9	02
04	240 50.3	20 31.2	300 30.8	04
06	270 50.2	20 32.2	330 35.7	06
08	300 50.1	20 33.1	0 40.6	08
10	330 50.0	20 34.1	30 45.6	10
12	0 49.9	20 35.0	60 50.5	12
14	30 49.8	20 36.0	90 55.4	14
16	60 49.7	20 36.9	121 00.4	16
18	90 49.6	20 37.9	151 05.3	18
20	120 49.4	20 38.8	181 10.2	20
22	150 49.3	N20 39.8	211 15.1	22

Monday, 28th May

h	SUN G.H.A.	Dec.	ARIES G.H.A.	h
00	180 42.9	N21 23.0	245 16.6	00
02	210 42.8	21 23.8	275 21.6	02
04	240 42.6	21 24.7	305 26.5	04
06	270 42.5	21 25.5	335 31.4	06
08	300 42.3	21 26.3	5 36.3	08
10	330 42.1	21 27.1	35 41.3	10
12	0 42.0	21 27.9	65 46.2	12
14	30 41.8	21 28.7	95 51.1	14
16	60 41.7	21 29.5	125 56.1	16
18	90 41.5	21 30.3	156 01.0	18
20	120 41.4	21 31.1	186 05.9	20
22	150 41.2	N21 31.9	216 10.8	22

Saturday, 19th May

h	SUN G.H.A.	Dec.	ARIES G.H.A.	h
00	180 54.2	N19 39.9	236 24.4	00
02	210 54.1	19 41.0	266 29.3	02
04	240 54.1	19 42.1	296 34.2	04
06	270 54.0	19 43.2	326 39.2	06
08	300 54.0	19 44.2	356 44.1	08
10	330 53.9	19 45.3	26 49.0	10
12	0 53.9	19 46.4	56 53.9	12
14	30 53.8	19 47.4	86 58.9	14
16	60 53.7	19 48.5	117 03.8	16
18	90 53.7	19 49.6	147 08.7	18
20	120 53.6	19 50.6	177 13.7	20
22	150 53.5	N19 51.7	207 18.6	22

Thursday, 24th May

h	SUN G.H.A.	Dec.	ARIES G.H.A.	h
00	180 49.2	N20 40.7	241 20.1	00
02	210 49.1	20 41.7	271 25.0	02
04	240 49.0	20 42.6	301 29.9	04
06	270 48.9	20 43.5	331 34.9	06
08	300 48.8	20 44.5	1 39.8	08
10	330 48.7	20 45.4	31 44.7	10
12	0 48.5	20 46.3	61 49.6	12
14	30 48.4	20 47.3	91 54.6	14
16	60 48.3	20 48.2	121 59.5	16
18	90 48.2	20 49.1	152 04.4	18
20	120 48.1	20 50.0	182 09.4	20
22	150 48.0	N20 50.9	212 14.3	22

Tuesday, 29th May

h	SUN G.H.A.	Dec.	ARIES G.H.A.	h
00	180 41.0	N21 32.7	246 15.8	00
02	210 40.9	21 33.5	276 20.7	02
04	240 40.7	21 34.2	306 25.6	04
06	270 40.6	21 35.0	336 30.5	06
08	300 40.4	21 35.8	6 35.5	08
10	330 40.2	21 36.6	36 40.4	10
12	0 40.1	21 37.4	66 45.3	12
14	30 39.9	21 38.1	96 50.3	14
16	60 39.7	21 38.9	126 55.2	16
18	90 39.6	21 39.7	157 00.1	18
20	120 39.4	21 40.4	187 05.0	20
22	150 39.2	N21 41.2	217 10.0	22

Sunday, 20th May

h	SUN G.H.A.	Dec.	ARIES G.H.A.	h
00	180 53.5	N19 52.8	237 23.5	00
02	210 53.4	19 53.8	267 28.4	02
04	240 53.3	19 54.9	297 33.4	04
06	270 53.3	19 55.9	327 38.3	06
08	300 53.2	19 57.0	357 43.2	08
10	330 53.1	19 58.0	27 48.2	10
12	0 53.1	19 59.1	57 53.1	12
14	30 53.0	20 00.1	87 58.0	14
16	60 52.9	20 01.1	118 02.9	16
18	90 52.8	20 02.2	148 07.9	18
20	120 52.8	20 03.2	178 12.8	20
22	150 52.7	N20 04.2	208 17.7	22

Friday, 25th May

h	SUN G.H.A.	Dec.	ARIES G.H.A.	h
00	180 47.8	N20 51.8	242 19.2	00
02	210 47.7	20 52.8	272 24.1	02
04	240 47.6	20 53.7	302 29.1	04
06	270 47.5	20 54.6	332 34.0	06
08	300 47.3	20 55.5	2 38.9	08
10	330 47.2	20 56.4	32 43.8	10
12	0 47.1	20 57.3	62 48.8	12
14	30 47.0	20 58.2	92 53.7	14
16	60 46.8	20 59.1	122 58.6	16
18	90 46.7	20 59.9	153 03.5	18
20	120 46.6	21 00.8	183 08.5	20
22	150 46.4	N21 01.7	213 13.4	22

Wednesday, 30th May

h	SUN G.H.A.	Dec.	ARIES G.H.A.	h
00	180 39.1	N21 42.0	247 14.9	00
02	210 38.9	21 42.7	277 19.8	02
04	240 38.7	21 43.5	307 24.8	04
06	270 38.5	21 44.2	337 29.7	06
08	300 38.4	21 45.0	7 34.6	08
10	330 38.2	21 45.7	37 39.5	10
12	0 38.0	21 46.5	67 44.5	12
14	30 37.9	21 47.2	97 49.4	14
16	60 37.7	21 47.9	127 54.3	16
18	90 37.5	21 48.7	157 59.3	18
20	120 37.3	21 49.4	188 04.2	20
22	150 37.1	N21 50.1	218 09.1	22

Thursday, 31st May

h	SUN G.H.A.	Dec.	ARIES G.H.A.	h
00	180 37.0	N21 50.9	248 14.0	00
02	210 36.8	21 51.6	278 19.0	02
04	240 36.6	21 52.3	308 23.9	04
06	270 36.4	N21 53.0	338 28.8	06
08	300 36.3	N21 53.6	8 33.8	08
10	330 36.1	21 54.5	38 38.7	10
12	0 35.9	21 55.2	68 43.6	12
14	30 35.7	N21 55.9	98 48.5	14
16	60 35.5	N21 56.5	128 53.5	16
18	90 35.3	21 57.3	158 58.4	18
20	120 35.2	21 58.0	189 03.3	20
22	150 35.0	N21 58.7	219 08.3	22

To interpolate SUN G.H.A. see page 4:7   To interpolate ARIES G.H.A. see page 4:8

3:66 ☉ SUN — October, 1990 — ARIES ♈

G.M.T.	SUN G.H.A.	SUN Dec.	ARIES G.H.A.	G.M.T.

Monday, 1st October

h	SUN G.H.A.	SUN Dec.	ARIES G.H.A.	h
00	182 31.5	S 3 00.1	9 28.1	00
02	212 31.9	3 02.0	39 33.1	02
04	242 32.3	3 04.0	69 38.0	04
06	272 32.7	3 06.9	99 42.9	06
08	302 33.1	3 07.9	129 47.8	08
10	332 33.5	3 08.8	159 52.8	10
12	2 33.9	3 11.7	189 57.7	12
14	32 34.3	3 13.7	220 02.6	14
16	62 34.7	3 15.6	250 07.6	16
18	92 35.1	3 17.5	280 12.5	18
20	122 35.5	3 19.5	310 17.4	20
22	152 35.9	S 3 21.4	340 22.3	22

Tuesday, 2nd October

h	SUN G.H.A.	SUN Dec.	ARIES G.H.A.	h
00	182 36.3	S 3 23.4	10 27.3	00
02	212 36.7	3 25.3	40 32.2	02
04	242 37.1	3 27.2	70 37.1	04
06	272 37.5	3 29.2	100 42.1	06
08	302 37.9	3 31.1	130 47.0	08
10	332 38.3	3 33.0	160 51.9	10
12	2 38.7	3 35.0	190 56.8	12
14	32 39.1	3 36.9	221 01.8	14
16	62 39.5	3 38.8	251 06.7	16
18	92 39.9	3 40.8	281 11.6	18
20	122 40.3	3 42.7	311 16.5	20
22	152 40.7	S 3 44.6	341 21.5	22

Wednesday, 3rd October

h	SUN G.H.A.	SUN Dec.	ARIES G.H.A.	h
00	182 41.1	S 3 46.6	11 26.4	00
02	212 41.5	3 48.5	41 31.3	02
04	242 41.9	3 50.4	71 36.3	04
06	272 42.3	3 52.4	101 41.2	06
08	302 42.7	3 54.3	131 46.1	08
10	332 43.1	3 56.2	161 51.0	10
12	2 43.5	3 58.2	191 56.0	12
14	32 43.9	4 00.1	222 00.9	14
16	62 44.3	4 02.0	252 05.8	16
18	92 44.7	4 04.0	282 10.8	18
20	122 45.1	4 05.9	312 15.7	20
22	152 45.4	S 4 07.8	342 20.6	22

Thursday, 4th October

h	SUN G.H.A.	SUN Dec.	ARIES G.H.A.	h
00	182 45.8	S 4 09.8	12 25.5	00
02	212 46.2	4 11.7	42 30.5	02
04	242 46.6	4 13.6	72 35.4	04
06	272 47.0	4 15.6	102 40.3	06
08	302 47.4	4 17.5	132 45.3	08
10	332 47.8	4 19.4	162 50.2	10
12	2 48.2	4 21.3	192 55.1	12
14	32 48.5	4 23.3	223 00.0	14
16	62 48.9	4 25.2	253 05.0	16
18	92 49.3	4 27.1	283 09.9	18
20	122 49.7	4 29.0	313 14.8	20
22	152 50.1	S 4 31.0	343 19.8	22

Friday, 5th October

h	SUN G.H.A.	SUN Dec.	ARIES G.H.A.	h
00	182 50.5	S 4 32.9	13 24.7	00
02	212 50.8	4 34.8	43 29.6	02
04	242 51.2	4 36.8	73 34.6	04
06	272 51.6	4 38.7	103 39.5	06
08	302 52.0	4 40.6	133 44.4	08
10	332 52.4	4 42.5	163 49.3	10
12	2 52.7	4 44.5	193 54.3	12
14	32 53.1	4 46.4	223 59.2	14
16	62 53.5	4 48.3	254 04.1	16
18	92 53.9	4 50.2	284 09.0	18
20	122 54.2	4 52.2	314 14.0	20
22	152 54.6	S 4 54.1	344 18.9	22

Saturday, 6th October

h	SUN G.H.A.	SUN Dec.	ARIES G.H.A.	h
00	182 55.0	S 4 56.0	14 23.8	00
02	212 55.4	4 57.9	44 28.8	02
04	242 55.8	4 59.8	74 33.7	04
06	272 56.1	5 01.7	104 38.6	06
08	302 56.5	5 03.7	134 43.5	08
10	332 56.9	5 05.6	164 48.5	10
12	2 57.2	5 07.5	194 53.4	12
14	32 57.6	5 09.4	224 58.3	14
16	62 58.0	5 11.3	255 03.2	16
18	92 58.3	5 13.3	285 08.2	18
20	122 58.7	5 15.2	315 13.1	20
22	152 59.1	S 5 17.1	345 18.0	22

Sunday, 7th October

h	SUN G.H.A.	SUN Dec.	ARIES G.H.A.	h
00	182 59.4	S 5 19.0	15 23.0	00
02	212 59.8	5 20.9	45 27.9	02
04	243 00.1	5 22.8	75 32.8	04
06	273 00.5	5 24.8	105 37.7	06
08	303 00.9	5 26.7	135 42.7	08
10	333 01.2	5 28.6	165 47.6	10
12	3 01.6	5 30.5	195 52.5	12
14	33 01.9	5 32.4	225 57.5	14
16	63 02.3	5 34.3	256 02.4	16
18	93 02.7	5 36.2	286 07.3	18
20	123 03.0	5 38.1	316 12.2	20
22	153 03.4	S 5 40.0	346 17.2	22

Monday, 8th October

h	SUN G.H.A.	SUN Dec.	ARIES G.H.A.	h
00	183 03.7	S 5 42.0	16 22.1	00
02	213 04.1	5 43.9	46 27.0	02
04	243 04.5	5 45.8	76 32.0	04
06	273 04.8	5 47.7	106 36.9	06
08	303 05.2	5 49.6	136 41.8	08
10	333 05.5	5 51.5	166 46.7	10
12	3 05.9	5 53.4	196 51.7	12
14	33 06.2	5 55.3	226 56.6	14
16	63 06.6	5 57.2	257 01.5	16
18	93 06.9	5 59.1	287 06.5	18
20	123 07.3	6 01.0	317 11.4	20
22	153 07.6	S 6 02.9	347 16.3	22

Tuesday, 9th October

h	SUN G.H.A.	SUN Dec.	ARIES G.H.A.	h
00	183 08.0	S 6 04.8	17 21.2	00
02	213 08.3	6 06.7	47 26.2	02
04	243 08.7	6 08.7	77 31.1	04
06	273 09.0	6 10.6	107 36.0	06
08	303 09.4	6 12.5	137 41.0	08
10	333 09.7	6 14.4	167 45.9	10
12	3 10.0	6 16.3	197 50.8	12
14	33 10.4	6 18.2	227 55.7	14
16	63 10.7	6 20.1	258 00.7	16
18	93 11.1	6 22.0	288 05.6	18
20	123 11.4	6 23.9	318 10.5	20
22	153 11.8	S 6 25.8	348 15.4	22

Wednesday, 10th October

h	SUN G.H.A.	SUN Dec.	ARIES G.H.A.	h
00	183 12.1	S 6 27.7	18 20.4	00
02	213 12.4	6 29.6	48 25.3	02
04	243 12.8	6 31.4	78 30.2	04
06	273 13.1	6 33.3	108 35.2	06
08	303 13.4	6 35.2	138 40.1	08
10	333 13.8	6 37.1	168 45.0	10
12	3 14.1	6 39.0	198 49.9	12
14	33 14.4	6 40.9	228 54.9	14
16	63 14.8	6 42.8	258 59.8	16
18	93 15.1	6 44.7	289 04.7	18
20	123 15.4	6 46.6	319 09.7	20
22	153 15.8	S 6 48.5	349 14.6	22

Thursday, 11th October

h	SUN G.H.A.	SUN Dec.	ARIES G.H.A.	h
00	183 16.1	S 6 50.4	19 19.5	00
02	213 16.4	6 52.3	49 24.4	02
04	243 16.8	6 54.2	79 29.4	04
06	273 17.1	6 56.0	109 34.3	06
08	303 17.4	6 57.9	139 39.2	08
10	333 17.7	6 59.8	169 44.2	10
12	3 18.1	7 01.7	199 49.1	12
14	33 18.4	7 03.6	229 54.0	14
16	63 18.7	7 05.5	259 58.9	16
18	93 19.0	7 07.4	290 03.9	18
20	123 19.3	7 09.2	320 08.8	20
22	153 19.7	S 7 11.1	350 13.7	22

Friday, 12th October

h	SUN G.H.A.	SUN Dec.	ARIES G.H.A.	h
00	183 20.0	S 7 13.0	20 18.7	00
02	213 20.3	7 14.9	50 23.6	02
04	243 20.6	7 16.8	80 28.5	04
06	273 20.9	7 18.7	110 33.4	06
08	303 21.2	7 20.5	140 38.4	08
10	333 21.6	7 22.4	170 43.3	10
12	3 21.9	7 24.3	200 48.2	12
14	33 22.2	7 26.2	230 53.2	14
16	63 22.5	7 28.1	260 58.1	16
18	93 22.8	7 29.9	291 03.0	18
20	123 23.1	7 31.8	321 07.9	20
22	153 23.4	S 7 33.7	351 12.9	22

Saturday, 13th October

h	SUN G.H.A.	SUN Dec.	ARIES G.H.A.	h
00	183 23.7	S 7 35.6	21 17.8	00
02	213 24.0	7 37.4	51 22.7	02
04	243 24.3	7 39.3	81 27.7	04
06	273 24.6	7 41.2	111 32.6	06
08	303 24.9	7 43.0	141 37.5	08
10	333 25.2	7 44.9	171 42.4	10
12	3 25.5	7 46.8	201 47.4	12
14	33 25.8	7 48.7	231 52.3	14
16	63 26.1	7 50.5	261 57.2	16
18	93 26.4	7 52.4	292 02.1	18
20	123 26.7	7 54.3	322 07.1	20
22	153 27.0	S 7 56.1	352 12.0	22

Sunday, 14th October

h	SUN G.H.A.	SUN Dec.	ARIES G.H.A.	h
00	183 27.3	S 7 58.0	22 16.9	00
02	213 27.6	7 59.9	52 21.9	02
04	243 27.9	8 01.7	82 26.8	04
06	273 28.2	8 03.6	112 31.7	06
08	303 28.5	8 05.4	142 36.6	08
10	333 28.8	8 07.3	172 41.6	10
12	3 29.1	8 09.2	202 46.5	12
14	33 29.4	8 11.0	232 51.4	14
16	63 29.6	8 12.9	262 56.4	16
18	93 29.9	8 14.7	293 01.3	18
20	123 30.2	8 16.6	323 06.2	20
22	153 30.5	S 8 18.5	353 11.1	22

Monday, 15th October

h	SUN G.H.A.	SUN Dec.	ARIES G.H.A.	h
00	183 30.8	S 8 20.3	23 16.1	00
02	213 31.1	8 22.2	53 21.0	02
04	243 31.4	8 24.0	83 25.9	04
06	273 31.6	8 25.9	113 30.9	06
08	303 31.9	8 27.7	143 35.8	08
10	333 32.2	8 29.6	173 40.7	10
12	3 32.5	8 31.4	203 45.6	12
14	33 32.8	8 33.3	233 50.6	14
16	63 33.0	8 35.1	263 55.5	16
18	93 33.3	8 37.0	294 00.4	18
20	123 33.6	8 38.8	324 05.4	20
22	153 33.9	S 8 40.7	354 10.3	22

To interpolate SUN G.H.A. see page 4:7   To interpolate ARIES G.H.A. see page 4:8

141

3:66 ☉ SUN — October, 1990 — ARIES ♈

Monday, 1st October

G.M.T. (h)	SUN G.H.A.	Dec.	ARIES G.H.A.	G.M.T. (h)
00	182 31.5	S 3 00.1	9 28.1	00
02	212 31.9	3 02.0	39 33.1	02
04	242 32.3	3 04.0	69 38.0	04
06	272 32.7	3 05.9	99 42.9	06
08	302 33.1	3 07.9	129 47.8	08
10	332 33.5	S 3 09.8	159 52.8	10
12	2 33.9	3 11.7	189 57.7	12
14	32 34.3	3 13.7	220 02.6	14
16	62 34.7	3 15.6	250 07.6	16
18	92 35.1	3 17.6	280 12.5	18
20	122 35.5	3 19.5	310 17.4	20
22	152 35.9	S 3 21.4	340 22.3	22

Tuesday, 2nd October

G.M.T. (h)	SUN G.H.A.	Dec.	ARIES G.H.A.	G.M.T. (h)
00	182 36.3	S 3 23.4	10 27.3	00
02	212 36.7	3 25.3	40 32.2	02
04	242 37.1	3 27.2	70 37.1	04
06	272 37.5	3 29.2	100 42.1	06
08	302 37.9	3 31.1	130 47.0	08
10	332 38.3	3 33.0	160 51.9	10
12	2 38.7	3 35.0	190 56.8	12
14	32 39.1	3 36.9	221 01.8	14
16	62 39.5	3 38.8	251 06.7	16
18	92 39.9	3 40.8	281 11.6	18
20	122 40.3	3 42.7	311 16.5	20
22	152 40.7	S 3 44.6	341 21.5	22

Wednesday, 3rd October

G.M.T. (h)	SUN G.H.A.	Dec.	ARIES G.H.A.	G.M.T. (h)
00	182 41.1	S 3 46.6	11 26.4	00
02	212 41.5	3 48.5	41 31.3	02
04	242 41.9	3 50.4	71 36.3	04
06	272 42.3	3 52.4	101 41.2	06
08	302 42.7	3 54.3	131 46.1	08
10	332 43.1	3 56.2	161 51.0	10
12	2 43.5	3 58.2	191 56.0	12
14	32 43.9	4 00.1	222 00.9	14
16	62 44.3	4 02.0	252 05.8	16
18	92 44.7	4 04.0	282 10.8	18
20	122 45.1	4 05.9	312 15.7	20
22	152 45.4	S 4 07.8	342 20.6	22

Thursday, 4th October

G.M.T. (h)	SUN G.H.A.	Dec.	ARIES G.H.A.	G.M.T. (h)
00	182 45.8	S 4 09.8	12 25.5	00
02	212 46.2	4 11.7	42 30.5	02
04	242 46.6	4 13.6	72 35.4	04
06	272 47.0	4 15.6	102 40.3	06
08	302 47.4	4 17.5	132 45.3	08
10	332 47.8	4 19.4	162 50.2	10
12	2 48.2	4 21.3	192 55.1	12
14	32 48.5	4 23.3	223 00.0	14
16	62 48.9	4 25.2	253 05.0	16
18	92 49.3	4 27.1	283 09.9	18
20	122 49.7	4 29.0	313 14.8	20
22	152 50.1	S 4 31.0	343 19.8	22

Friday, 5th October

G.M.T. (h)	SUN G.H.A.	Dec.	ARIES G.H.A.	G.M.T. (h)
00	182 50.5	S 4 32.9	13 24.7	00
02	212 50.8	4 34.8	43 29.6	02
04	242 51.2	4 36.8	73 34.5	04
06	272 51.6	4 38.7	103 39.5	06
08	302 52.0	4 40.6	133 44.4	08
10	332 52.4	4 42.5	163 49.3	10
12	2 52.7	4 44.5	193 54.3	12
14	32 53.1	4 46.4	223 59.2	14
16	62 53.5	4 48.3	254 04.1	16
18	92 53.9	4 50.2	284 09.0	18
20	122 54.2	4 52.2	314 14.0	20
22	152 54.6	S 4 54.1	344 18.9	22

Saturday, 6th October

G.M.T. (h)	SUN G.H.A.	Dec.	ARIES G.H.A.	G.M.T. (h)
00	182 55.0	S 4 56.0	14 23.8	00
02	212 55.4	4 57.9	44 28.8	02
04	242 55.8	4 59.8	74 33.7	04
06	272 56.1	5 01.7	104 38.6	06
08	302 56.5	5 03.7	134 43.5	08
10	332 56.9	5 05.6	164 48.5	10
12	2 57.2	5 07.5	194 53.4	12
14	32 57.6	5 09.4	224 58.3	14
16	62 58.0	5 11.3	255 03.2	16
18	92 58.3	5 13.3	285 08.2	18
20	122 58.7	5 15.2	315 13.1	20
22	152 59.1	S 5 17.1	345 18.0	22

Sunday, 7th October

G.M.T. (h)	SUN G.H.A.	Dec.	ARIES G.H.A.	G.M.T. (h)
00	182 59.4	S 5 19.0	15 23.0	00
02	212 59.8	5 20.9	45 27.9	02
04	243 00.1	5 22.8	75 32.8	04
06	273 00.5	5 24.8	105 37.7	06
08	303 00.9	5 26.7	135 42.7	08
10	333 01.2	5 28.6	165 47.6	10
12	3 01.6	5 30.5	195 52.5	12
14	33 01.9	5 32.4	225 57.5	14
16	63 02.3	5 34.3	258 02.4	16
18	93 02.7	5 36.2	286 07.3	18
20	123 03.0	5 38.1	316 12.2	20
22	153 03.4	S 5 40.0	346 17.2	22

Monday, 8th October

G.M.T. (h)	SUN G.H.A.	Dec.	ARIES G.H.A.	G.M.T. (h)
00	183 03.7	S 5 42.0	16 22.1	00
02	213 04.1	5 43.9	46 27.0	02
04	243 04.4	5 45.8	76 32.0	04
06	273 04.8	5 47.7	106 36.9	06
08	303 05.2	5 49.6	136 41.8	08
10	333 05.5	5 51.5	166 46.7	10
12	3 05.9	5 53.4	196 51.7	12
14	33 06.2	5 55.3	226 56.6	14
16	63 06.6	5 57.2	257 01.5	16
18	93 06.9	5 59.1	287 06.5	18
20	123 07.3	6 01.0	317 11.4	20
22	153 07.6	S 6 02.9	347 16.3	22

Tuesday, 9th October

G.M.T. (h)	SUN G.H.A.	Dec.	ARIES G.H.A.	G.M.T. (h)
00	183 08.0	S 6 04.8	17 21.2	00
02	213 08.3	6 06.7	47 26.2	02
04	243 08.7	6 08.7	77 31.1	04
06	273 09.0	6 10.6	107 36.0	06
08	303 09.4	6 12.5	137 41.0	08
10	333 09.7	6 14.4	167 45.9	10
12	3 10.1	6 16.3	197 50.8	12
14	33 10.4	6 18.2	227 55.7	14
16	63 10.7	6 20.1	258 00.7	16
18	93 11.1	6 22.0	288 05.6	18
20	123 11.4	6 23.9	318 10.5	20
22	153 11.8	S 6 25.8	348 15.4	22

Wednesday, 10th October

G.M.T. (h)	SUN G.H.A.	Dec.	ARIES G.H.A.	G.M.T. (h)
00	183 12.1	S 6 27.7	18 20.4	00
02	213 12.4	6 29.6	48 25.3	02
04	243 12.8	6 31.4	78 30.2	04
06	273 13.1	6 33.3	108 35.2	06
08	303 13.4	6 35.2	138 40.1	08
10	333 13.8	6 37.1	168 45.0	10
12	3 14.1	6 39.0	198 49.9	12
14	33 14.4	6 40.9	228 54.9	14
16	63 14.8	6 42.8	258 59.8	16
18	93 15.1	6 44.7	289 04.7	18
20	123 15.4	6 46.6	319 09.7	20
22	153 15.8	S 6 48.5	349 14.6	22

Thursday, 11th October

G.M.T. (h)	SUN G.H.A.	Dec.	ARIES G.H.A.	G.M.T. (h)
00	183 16.1	S 6 50.4	19 19.5	00
02	213 16.4	6 52.3	49 24.4	02
04	243 16.8	6 54.2	79 29.4	04
06	273 17.1	6 56.0	109 34.3	06
08	303 17.4	6 57.9	139 39.2	08
10	333 17.7	6 59.8	169 44.2	10
12	3 18.1	7 01.7	199 49.1	12
14	33 18.4	7 03.6	229 54.0	14
16	63 18.7	7 05.5	259 58.9	16
18	93 19.0	7 07.4	290 03.9	18
20	123 19.3	7 09.2	320 08.8	20
22	153 19.7	S 7 11.1	350 13.7	22

Friday, 12th October

G.M.T. (h)	SUN G.H.A.	Dec.	ARIES G.H.A.	G.M.T. (h)
00	183 20.0	S 7 13.0	20 18.7	00
02	213 20.3	7 14.9	50 23.6	02
04	243 20.6	7 16.8	80 28.5	04
06	273 20.9	7 18.7	110 33.4	06
08	303 21.2	7 20.5	140 38.4	08
10	333 21.6	7 22.4	170 43.3	10
12	3 21.9	7 24.3	200 48.2	12
14	33 22.2	7 26.2	230 53.2	14
16	63 22.5	7 28.1	260 58.1	16
18	93 22.8	7 29.9	291 03.0	18
20	123 23.1	7 31.8	321 07.9	20
22	153 23.4	S 7 33.7	351 12.9	22

Saturday, 13th October

G.M.T. (h)	SUN G.H.A.	Dec.	ARIES G.H.A.	G.M.T. (h)
00	183 23.7	S 7 35.6	21 17.8	00
02	213 24.0	7 37.4	51 22.7	02
04	243 24.3	7 39.3	81 27.7	04
06	273 24.6	7 41.2	111 32.6	06
08	303 24.9	7 43.0	141 37.5	08
10	333 25.2	7 44.9	171 42.4	10
12	3 25.5	7 46.8	201 47.4	12
14	33 25.8	7 48.7	231 52.3	14
16	63 26.1	7 50.5	261 57.2	16
18	93 26.4	7 52.4	292 02.1	18
20	123 26.7	7 54.3	322 07.1	20
22	153 27.0	S 7 56.1	352 12.0	22

Sunday, 14th October

G.M.T. (h)	SUN G.H.A.	Dec.	ARIES G.H.A.	G.M.T. (h)
00	183 27.3	S 7 58.0	22 16.9	00
02	213 27.6	7 59.9	52 21.9	02
04	243 27.9	8 01.7	82 26.8	04
06	273 28.2	8 03.6	112 31.7	06
08	303 28.5	8 05.4	142 36.6	08
10	333 28.8	8 07.3	172 41.6	10
12	3 29.1	8 09.2	202 46.5	12
14	33 29.4	8 11.0	232 51.4	14
16	63 29.7	8 12.9	262 56.4	16
18	93 29.9	8 14.7	293 01.3	18
20	123 30.2	8 16.6	323 06.2	20
22	153 30.5	S 8 18.5	353 11.1	22

Monday, 15th October

G.M.T. (h)	SUN G.H.A.	Dec.	ARIES G.H.A.	G.M.T. (h)
00	183 30.8	S 8 20.3	23 16.1	00
02	213 31.1	8 22.2	53 21.0	02
04	243 31.4	8 24.0	83 25.9	04
06	273 31.6	8 25.9	113 30.9	06
08	303 31.9	8 27.7	143 35.8	08
10	333 32.2	8 29.6	173 40.7	10
12	3 32.5	8 31.4	203 45.6	12
14	33 32.8	8 33.3	233 50.6	14
16	63 33.0	8 35.1	263 55.5	16
18	93 33.3	8 37.0	294 00.4	18
20	123 33.6	8 38.8	324 05.4	20
22	153 33.9	S 8 40.7	354 10.3	22

To interpolate SUN G.H.A. see page 4:7   To interpolate ARIES G.H.A. see page 4:8

3:38 Oh. G.M.T. (Midnight)   **MAY, 1990**   Oh. G.M.T. (Midnight)

♀ VENUS ♀ | JUPITER ♃

Mer. Pass.	G.H.A.	Mean Var. 14°	Dec.	Mean Var.	M.	Day of Week	G.H.A.	Mean Var. 15°	Dec.	Mean Var.	Mer. Pass.
h. m.	° '	'	° '	'			° '	'	° '	'	h. m.
09 14	221 26.2	59.9	S 2 28.5	1.0	1	Tu.	121 05.9	2.0	N23 22.9	0.0	15 53
09 15	221 22.7	59.9	S 2 05.0	1.0	2	Wed.	121 54.0	2.0	N23 22.5	0.0	15 50
09 15	221 19.1	59.9	S 1 41.3	1.0	3	Th.	122 41.9	2.0	N23 22.0	0.0	15 47
09 15	221 15.4	59.8	S 1 17.5	1.0	4	Fri.	123 29.8	2.0	N23 21.5	0.0	15 44
09 15	221 11.7	59.8	S 0 53.5	1.0	5	Sat.	124 17.6	2.0	N23 21.0	0.0	15 41
09 15	221 07.9	59.8	S 0 29.4	1.0	6	SUN.	125 05.3	2.0	N23 20.5	0.0	15 38
09 15	221 04.1	59.8	S 0 05.2	1.0	7	Mon.	125 52.9	2.0	N23 19.9	0.0	15 34
09 16	221 00.2	59.8	N 0 19.2	1.0	8	Tu.	126 40.4	2.0	N23 19.4	0.0	15 31
09 16	220 56.1	59.8	N 0 43.6	1.0	9	Wed.	127 27.8	2.0	N23 18.8	0.0	15 28
09 16	220 52.1	59.8	N 1 08.2	1.0	10	Th.	128 15.1	2.0	N23 18.2	0.0	15 25
09 17	220 47.9	59.8	N 1 32.9	1.0	11	Fri.	129 02.3	2.0	N23 17.5	0.0	15 22
09 17	220 43.6	59.8	N 1 57.6	1.0	12	Sat.	129 49.5	2.0	N23 16.9	0.0	15 19
09 17	220 39.2	59.8	N 2 22.4	1.0	13	SUN.	130 36.5	2.0	N23 16.2	0.0	15 15
09 18	220 34.8	59.8	N 2 47.2	1.0	14	Mon.	131 23.5	2.0	N23 15.5	0.0	15 12
09 18	220 30.2	59.8	N 3 12.1	1.0	15	Tu.	132 10.4	2.0	N23 14.8	0.0	15 09
09 18	220 25.5	59.8	N 3 37.0	1.0	16	Wed.	132 57.2	1.9	N23 14.1	0.0	15 06
09 19	220 20.6	59.8	N 4 01.9	1.0	17	Thu.	133 43.9	1.9	N23 13.3	0.0	15 03
09 19	220 15.7	59.8	N 4 26.8	1.0	18	Fri.	134 30.6	1.9	N23 12.6	0.0	15 00
09 19	220 10.6	59.8	N 4 51.8	1.0	19	Sat.	135 17.1	1.9	N23 11.8	0.0	14 57
09 20	220 05.4	59.8	N 5 16.7	1.0	20	SUN.	136 03.6	1.9	N23 10.9	0.0	14 54
09 20	220 00.0	59.8	N 5 41.6	1.0	21	Mon.	136 50.1	1.9	N23 10.1	0.0	14 51
09 20	219 54.5	59.8	N 6 06.4	1.0	22	Tu.	137 36.4	1.9	N23 09.2	0.0	14 48
09 21	219 48.8	59.8	N 6 31.2	1.0	23	Wed.	138 22.7	1.9	N23 08.3	0.0	14 45
09 21	219 43.0	59.8	N 6 56.0	1.0	24	Th.	139 09.0	1.9	N23 07.4	0.0	14 42
09 21	219 37.0	59.7	N 7 20.6	1.0	25	Fri.	139 55.1	1.9	N23 06.5	0.0	14 38
09 21	219 30.9	59.7	N 7 45.2	1.0	26	Sat.	140 41.2	1.9	N23 05.6	0.0	14 35
09 22	219 24.5	59.7	N 8 09.7	1.0	27	SUN.	141 27.3	1.9	N23 04.6	0.0	14 32
09 22	219 18.0	59.7	N 8 34.1	1.0	28	Mon.	142 13.2	1.9	N23 03.6	0.0	14 29
09 23	219 11.3	95.7	N 8 58.4	1.0	29	Tu.	142 59.2	1.9	N23 02.6	0.0	14 26
09 23	219 04.5	59.7	N 9 22.5	1.0	30	Wed.	143 45.0	1.9	N23 01.5	0.0	14 23
09 24	218 57.4	59.7	N 9 46.5	1.0	31	Th.	144 30.8	1.9	N23 00.4	0.0	14 20

♀ **VENUS.** Av. Mag. -4.1. A Morning Star. S.H.A. May 5 359°; 10 353°; 15 348°; 20 343°; 25 337°; 30 332°.

♃ **JUPITER.** Av. Mag. -1.9. An Evening Star. S.H.A. May 5 262°; 10 262°; 15 259°; 20 259°; 25 258°; 30 256°.

♂ MARS ♂ | MAY | ♄ SATURN ♄

Mer. Pass.	G.H.A.	Mean Var. 15°	Dec.	Mean Var.	M.	Day of Week	G.H.A.	Mean Var. 15°	Dec.	Mean Var.	Mer. Pass.
h. m.	° '	'	° '	'			° '	'	° '	'	h. m.
08 04	238 51.0	0.7	S10 12.0	0.7	1	Tu.	281 24.7	2.5	S20 54.4	0.0	05 14
08 03	239 07.7	0.7	S 9 55.8	0.7	2	Wed.	282 23.5	2.5	S20 54.4	0.0	05 10
08 02	239 24.4	0.7	S 9 39.7	0.7	3	Th.	283 22.4	2.5	S20 54.4	0.0	05 06
08 01	239 41.3	0.7	S 9 23.4	0.7	4	Fri.	284 21.3	2.5	S20 54.5	0.0	05 02
08 00	239 58.2	0.7	S 9 07.1	0.7	5	Sat.	285 20.4	2.5	S20 54.5	0.0	04 58
07 58	240 15.2	0.7	S 8 50.7	0.7	6	SUN.	286 19.6	2.5	S20 54.6	0.0	04 54
07 57	240 32.3	0.7	S 8 34.3	0.7	7	Mon.	287 18.9	2.5	S20 54.7	0.0	04 50
07 56	240 49.4	0.7	S 8 17.8	0.7	8	Tu.	288 18.3	2.5	S20 54.8	0.0	04 46
07 55	241 06.6	0.7	S 8 01.2	0.7	9	Wed.	289 17.7	2.5	S20 54.9	0.0	04 42
07 54	241 23.9	0.7	S 7 44.6	0.7	10	Th.	290 17.3	2.5	S20 55.1	0.0	04 38
07 53	241 41.3	0.7	S 7 27.9	0.7	11	Fri.	291 17.0	2.5	S20 55.2	0.0	04 34
07 52	241 58.7	0.7	S 7 11.2	0.7	12	Sat.	292 16.8	2.5	S20 55.4	0.0	04 30
07 50	242 16.2	0.7	S 6 54.4	0.7	13	SUN.	293 16.7	2.5	S20 55.6	0.0	04 26
07 49	242 33.7	0.7	S 6 37.6	0.7	14	Mon.	294 16.7	2.5	S20 55.8	0.0	04 22
07 48	242 51.3	0.7	S 6 20.8	0.7	15	Tu.	295 16.8	2.5	S20 56.1	0.0	04 18
07 47	243 09.0	0.7	S 6 03.9	0.7	16	Wed.	296 17.0	2.5	S20 56.3	0.0	04 14
07 46	243 26.8	0.7	S 5 47.0	0.7	17	Th.	297 17.3	2.5	S20 56.6	0.0	04 10
07 45	243 44.6	0.7	S 5 30.1	0.7	18	Fri.	298 17.7	2.5	S20 56.9	0.0	04 06
07 44	244 02.4	0.7	S 5 13.1	0.7	19	Sat.	299 18.2	2.5	S20 57.2	0.0	04 02
07 42	244 20.3	0.7	S 4 56.1	0.7	20	SUN.	300 18.8	2.5	S20 57.5	0.0	03 58
07 41	244 38.3	0.7	S 4 39.1	0.7	21	Mon.	301 19.5	2.5	S20 57.8	0.0	03 54
07 40	244 56.4	0.8	S 4 22.1	0.7	22	Tu.	302 20.2	2.5	S20 58.2	0.0	03 50
07 39	245 14.5	0.8	S 4 05.0	0.7	23	Wed.	303 21.1	2.5	S20 58.6	0.0	03 46
07 37	245 32.6	0.8	S 3 48.0	0.7	24	Th.	304 22.1	2.5	S20 58.9	0.0	03 42
07 36	245 50.8	0.8	S 3 30.9	0.7	25	Fri.	305 23.2	2.6	S20 59.3	0.0	03 38
07 35	246 09.1	0.8	S 3 13.8	0.7	26	Sat.	306 24.3	2.6	S20 59.8	0.0	03 34
07 33	246 27.4	0.8	S 2 56.8	0.7	27	SUN.	307 25.6	2.6	S21 00.2	0.0	03 30
07 32	246 45.8	0.8	S 2 39.7	0.7	28	Mon.	308 26.9	2.6	S21 00.6	0.0	03 26
07 31	247 04.3	0.8	S 2 22.6	0.7	29	Tu.	309 28.4	2.6	S21 01.1	0.0	03 22
07 30	247 22.8	0.8	S 2 05.6	0.7	30	Wed.	310 29.9	2.6	S21 01.6	0.0	03 18
07 29	247 41.3	0.8	S 1 48.5	0.7	31	Th.	311 31.5	2.6	S21 02.1	0.0	03 13

♂ **MARS.** Av. Mag. +0.7. A Morning Star. S.H.A. May 17°; 10 14°; 15 10°; 20 7°; 25 4°; 30 0°.

♄ **SATURN.** Av. Mag. +0.4. Can be seen throughout the month in the morning. S.H.A. May 5 63°; 10 64°; 15 62°; 20 63°; 25 64°; 30 62°.

MERCURY. Too close to the sun for observation until May 13 when it can be seen low in the east before sunrise.

For Planets Correction Tables see pages 4:9-4:13. See also 'How to Recognise the Planets' on page 2:32.
Mean Var. means Variation per Hour.

3:34 **MAY, 1990**

G.M.T. (31 days) G.M.T.

☉ SUN ☉

DATE Yr.	Mth.	Week	Equation of Time 0 h. m. s.	12 h. m. s.	Transit h. m.	Semidiam. '	Lat. 52°N. Twilight h. m.	Sunrise h. m.	Sunset h. m.	Twilight h. m.	Lat. Corr. Lat. °	Twilight h. m.	Sunrise h. m.	Sunset h. m.	Twilight h. m.
121	1	Tu	−02 51	−02 54	11 57	15.9	03 52	04 31	19 24	20 03	N70	T.A.N.	−3 17	+3 32	T.A.N.
122	2	W	−02 58	−03 01	11 57	15.9	03 50	04 29	19 26	20 05	68	T.A.N.	−2 16	+2 20	T.A.N.
123	3	Th	−03 05	−03 08	11 57	15.9	03 48	04 27	19 28	20 07	66	T.A.N.	−1 42	+1 45	T.A.N.
124	4	F	−03 11	−03 14	11 57	15.9	03 46	04 25	19 29	20 09	64	−2 12	−1 17	+1 20	+2 13
125	5	Sa	−03 17	−03 19	11 57	15.9	03 44	04 23	19 31	20 11	62	−1 31	−0 58	+1 01	+1 31
126	6	Sun	−03 22	−03 24	11 57	15.9	03 42	04 21	19 33	20 13	N60	−1 04	−0 43	+0 44	+1 03
127	7	M	−03 26	−03 28	11 57	15.9	03 40	04 20	19 34	20 14	58	−0 42	−0 30	+0 30	+0 45
128	8	Tu	−03 30	−03 32	11 56	15.9	03 38	04 18	19 36	20 16	56	−0 27	−0 18	+0 19	+0 27
129	9	W	−03 34	−03 35	11 56	15.9	03 36	04 16	19 38	20 18	54	−0 12	−0 08	+0 09	+0 12
130	10	Th	−03 37	−03 38	11 56	15.9	03 34	04 15	19 39	20 20	50	+0 11	+0 08	−0 08	−0 11
131	11	F	−03 39	−03 40	11 56	15.9	03 32	04 13	19 41	20 22	N45	+0 33	+0 25	−0 24	−0 32
132	12	Sa	−03 41	−03 41	11 56	15.9	03 30	04 11	19 42	20 24	40	+0 50	+0 39	−0 38	−0 49
133	13	Sun	−03 42	−03 42	11 56	15.8	03 28	04 10	19 44	20 26	35	+1 04	+0 50	−0 50	−1 03
134	14	M	−03 43	−03 43	11 56	15.8	03 26	04 08	19 45	20 28	30	+1 17	+1 00	−1 00	−1 16
135	15	Tu	−03 43	−03 42	11 56	15.8	03 24	04 07	19 47	20 30	20	+1 35	+1 17	−1 17	−1 35
136	16	W	−03 42	−03 42	11 56	15.8	03 23	04 05	19 48	20 31	N10	+1 51	+1 32	−1 32	−1 51
137	17	Th	−03 41	−03 40	11 56	15.8	03 21	04 04	19 50	20 33	0	+2 06	+1 46	−1 46	−2 06
138	18	F	−03 39	−03 38	11 56	15.8	03 19	04 02	19 51	20 35	S10	+2 19	+1 59	−2 00	−2 19
139	19	Sa	−03 37	−03 35	11 56	15.8	03 18	04 01	19 53	20 36	20	+2 32	+2 15	−2 15	−2 32
140	20	Sun	−03 34	−03 32	11 56	15.8	03 16	03 59	19 54	20 38	S35	+2 46	+2 30	−2 31	−2 47
141	21	M	−03 31	−03 29	11 56	15.8	03 14	03 58	19 56	20 40	40	+3 03	+2 50	−2 52	−3 03
142	22	Tu	−03 27	−03 24	11 57	15.8	03 13	03 57	19 57	20 41	S50	+3 24	+3 18	−3 04	−3 24
143	23	W	−03 22	−03 20	11 57	15.8	03 11	03 56	19 59	20 43					
144	24	Th	−03 17	−03 14	11 57	15.8	03 10	03 55	20 00	20 45					
145	25	F	−03 11	−03 08	11 57	15.8	03 08	03 53	20 02	20 46					
146	26	Sa	−03 05	−03 02	11 57	15.8	03 07	03 52	20 03	20 48		**NOTES**			
147	27	Sun	−02 59	−02 55	11 57	15.8	03 06	03 51	20 04	20 49					
148	28	M	−02 52	−02 48	11 57	15.8	03 04	03 50	20 06	20 51		The Lat. Corr. to sunrise, sunset, etc.,			
149	29	Tu	−02 44	−02 40	11 57	15.8	03 03	03 49	20 07	20 52		is for the middle of May. T.A.N. means			
150	30	W	−02 36	−02 32	11 57	15.8	03 02	03 48	20 08	20 54		Twilight all night. Examples are given			
151	31	Th	−02 28	−02 24	11 58	15.8	03 01	03 47	20 10	20 55		on page 2:11 onwards.			

Equation of Time is the excess of Mean Time over Apparent Time
(See explanation and examples on p. 2:15.)

☾ MOON ☽

DATE Yr.	Mth.	Week	Age days	Transit Diff. (Upper) h. m.	m.	Semidiam. '	Hor. Par. 12 h. '	Lat.52°N. Moonrise h. m.	Moonset h. m.
121	1	Tu	06	18 13	47	15.7	57.6	10 10	01 34
122	2	W	07	19 00	44	15.5	56.8	11 30	01 55
123	3	Th	08	19 44	44	15.3	56.0	12 47	02 11
124	4	F	09	20 28	42	15.1	55.4	14 01	02 24
125	5	Sa	10	21 07	41	15.0	54.9	15 13	02 36
126	6	Sun	11	21 48	41	14.9	54.5	16 24	02 47
127	7	M	12	22 29	41	14.8	54.2	17 35	02 59
128	8	Tu	13	23 13	46	14.7	54.1	18 47	03 13
129	9	W	14	23 59	48	14.7	54.0	19 59	03 30
130	10	Th	15	24 47	—	14.7	54.0	21 08	03 52
131	11	F	16	00 47	51	14.7	54.1	22 11	04 22
132	12	Sa	17	01 38	51	14.8	54.2	23 05	05 02
133	13	Sun	18	02 29	51	14.9	54.5	23 47	05 55
134	14	M	19	03 20	50	15.0	54.9	—	06 59
135	15	Tu	20	04 10	49	15.1	55.6	00 18	08 10
136	16	W	21	04 59	47	15.3	56.1	00 42	09 26
137	17	Th	22	05 46	47	15.5	56.9	01 01	10 44
138	18	F	23	06 33	46	15.7	57.7	01 18	12 04
139	19	Sa	24	07 19	47	16.0	58.6	01 30	13 24
140	20	Sun	25	08 06	50	16.2	59.5	01 43	14 48
141	21	M	26	08 56	54	16.4	60.3	01 58	16 16
142	22	Tu	27	09 50	59	16.6	60.9	02 16	17 48
143	23	W	28	10 49	64	16.7	61.3	02 39	19 22
144	24	Th	00	11 53	66	16.7	61.3	03 11	20 50
145	25	F	01	12 59	66	16.6	61.1	03 58	22 04
146	26	Sa	02	14 05	62	16.5	60.5	05 03	22 57
147	27	Sun	03	15 07	57	16.3	59.7	06 23	23 33
148	28	M	04	16 04	50	16.0	58.8	07 48	23 58
149	29	Tu	05	16 54	43	15.7	57.8	09 13	—
150	30	W	06	16 54	43	15.5	56.9	10 33	00 16
151	31	Th	07	18 24	42	15.3	56.1	11 49	00 30

MOON'S PHASES

		d.	h.	m.
☽	First Quarter	1	20	18
○	Full Moon	9	19	31
☾	Last Quarter	17	19	45
●	New Moon	24	11	47
☽	First Quarter	31	08	11

	d.	h.
Apogee	10	00
Perigee	24	03

NOTES

Moon's G.H.A. and Dec. are given on page 3:39.
A table for correcting Moonrise and Moonset for latitude is on page 4:20.
A table for correcting Moon's meridian passage (transit) for longitude is on page 4:19.
Examples on the use of the above data are given on page 2:11 onwards.

0h. = midnight. For explanation of use of above data see page 2:11 onwards.

3:64   **OCTOBER, 1990**

G.M.T.   **(31 days)**   G.M.T.

☉ SUN ☉

DATE			Equation of Time		Transit	Semi-diam.	Lat. 52°N.				Lat. Corr. to Sunrise, Sunset, etc.				
Day of			0 h.	12 h.			Twilight	Sunrise	Sunset	Twilight	Lat.	Twilight	Sunrise	Sunset	Twilight
Yr.	Mth.	Week	m. s.	m. s.	h. m.	′	h. m.	h. m.	h. m.	h. m.	°	h. m.	h. m.	h. m.	h. m.
274	1	M	−10 06	−10 15	11 50	16.0	05 26	06 00	17 38	18 11	N70	+0 19	+0 49	−0 51	−0 20
275	2	Tu	−10 25	−10 35	11 49	16.0	05 28	06 02	17 36	18 09	68	+0 16	+0 40	−0 41	−0 16
276	3	W	−10 44	−10 54	11 49	16.0	05 30	06 04	17 34	18 07	66	+0 13	+0 32	−0 33	−0 14
277	4	Th	−11 03	−11 12	11 49	16.0	05 31	08 05	17 31	18 05	64	+0 10	+0 25	−0 27	−0 11
278	5	F	−11 21	−11 31	11 48	16.0	05 33	06 07	17 29	18 03	62	+0 08	+0 20	−0 21	−0 09
279	6	Sa	−11 40	−11 49	11 48	16.0	05 35	06 09	17 27	18 01	N60	+0 06	+0 14	−0 16	−0 07
280	7	Sun	−11 57	−12 06	11 48	16.0	05 36	06 10	17 24	17 58	58	+0 05	+0 10	−0 11	−0 05
281	8	M	−12 15	−12 23	11 48	16.0	05 38	06 12	17 22	17 56	56	+0 03	+0 06	−0 07	−0 04
282	9	Tu	−12 32	−12 40	11 47	16.0	05 40	06 14	17 20	17 54	54	+0 01	+0 03	−0 04	−0 02
283	10	W	−12 48	−12 56	11 47	16.0	05 41	06 15	17 18	17 51	50	−0 02	−0 03	+0 03	+0 01
284	11	Th	−13 04	−13 12	11 47	16.0	05 43	06 17	17 16	17 49	N45	−0 05	−0 10	+0 09	+0 05
285	12	F	−13 20	−13 27	11 47	16.0	05 45	06 19	17 14	17 47	40	−0 08	−0 15	+0 14	+0 07
286	13	Sa	−13 35	−13 42	11 46	16.1	05 46	06 20	17 11	17 45	35	−0 11	−0 19	+0 19	+0 10
287	14	Sun	−13 49	−13 56	11 46	16.1	05 48	08 22	17 09	17 43	30	−0 14	−0 23	+0 23	+0 13
288	15	M	−14 03	−14 10	11 46	16.1	05 50	06 24	17 07	17 41	20	−0 18	−0 30	+0 30	+0 18
289	16	Tu	−14 16	−14 23	11 46	16.1	05 51	06 26	17 04	17 39	N10	−0 24	−0 36	+0 37	+0 23
290	17	W	−14 29	−14 35	11 45	16.1	05 53	06 28	17 02	17 37	0	−0 29	−0 42	+0 43	+0 29
291	18	Th	−14 41	−14 47	11 45	16.1	05 55	06 30	17 00	17 35	S10	−0 36	−0 49	+0 49	+0 36
292	19	F	−14 53	−14 58	11 45	16.1	05 56	06 31	16 58	17 32	20	−0 43	−0 55	+0 57	+0 44
293	20	Sa	−15 04	−15 09	11 45	16.1	05 58	06 33	16 56	17 30	30	−0 53	−1 03	+1 05	+0 54
294	21	Sun	−15 14	−15 19	11 45	16.1	06 00	06 35	16 54	17 28	S35	−1 00	−1 08	+1 10	+1 00
295	22	M	−15 24	−15 28	11 45	16.1	06 02	06 36	16 52	17 26	40	−1 07	−1 13	+1 15	+1 08
296	23	Tu	−15 33	−15 37	11 44	16.1	06 04	06 38	16 50	17 24	45	−1 16	−1 19	+1 21	+1 16
297	24	W	−15 41	−15 45	11 44	16.1	06 06	06 40	16 48	17 22	S50	−1 27	−1 27	+1 28	+1 26
298	25	Th	−15 49	−15 52	11 44	16.1	06 07	06 42	16 46	17 21					
299	26	F	−15 56	−15 59	11 44	16.1	06 09	06 44	16 44	17 19					
300	27	Sa	−16 02	−16 05	11 44	16.1	06 11	06 46	16 42	17 17					
301	28	Sun	−16 07	−16 10	11 44	16.1	06 12	06 47	16 40	17 15					
302	29	M	−16 12	−16 14	11 44	16.1	06 14	06 49	16 38	17 13					
303	30	Tu	−16 16	−16 18	11 44	16.1	06 16	06 51	16 36	17 11					
304	31	W	−16 20	−16 21	11 44	16.1	06 17	06 52	16 34	17 10					

NOTES
The Lat. Corr. to sunrise, sunset, etc., is for the middle of October. Examples on the use of the above data are given on page 2:11 onwards.

Equation of Time is the excess of Mean Time over Apparent Time (See explanation and examples on p. 2:15.)

☾ MOON ☽

DATE			Age	Transit Diff. (Upper)	Semi-diam.	Hor. Par. 12 h.	Lat. 52°N.		MOON'S PHASES
Day of			days				Moon-rise	Moon set	
Yr.	Mth.	Week		h. m. m.	′	′	h. m.	h. m.	
274	1	M	12	21 40 47	15.7	57.5	16 17	01 58	
275	2	Tu	13	22 27 49	15.9	58.4	16 31	03 18	○ Full Moon .... d. 4 h. 12 m. 02
276	3	W	14	23 16 51	16.1	59.1	16 46	04 40	
277	4	Th	15	24 07 54	16.3	59.8	17 01	06 05	☾ Last Quarter 11 03 31
278	5	F	16	00 07 58	16.4	60.2	17 20	07 33	● New Moon 18 15 37
279	6	Sa	17	01 01 58	16.4	60.4	17 44	09 03	
280	7	Sun	18	01 58 61	16.4	60.3	18 18	10 33	☽ First Quarter 26 20 26
281	8	M	19	03 00 62	16.4	60.0	19 05	11 56	
282	9	Tu	20	04 03 63	16.2	59.6	20 08	13 04	
283	10	W	21	05 06 63	16.1	59.1	21 24	13 54	d. h.
284	11	Th	22	06 05 59	15.9	58.5	22 46	14 29	
285	12	F	23	07 00 50	15.8	57.9	—	14 54	Perigee 6 18
286	13	Sa	24	07 50 47	15.6	57.4	00 09	15 13	Apogee 22 16
287	14	Sun	25	08 37 45	15.5	56.8	01 29	15 28	
288	15	M	26	09 22 43	15.3	56.3	02 46	15 41	
289	16	Tu	27	10 05 42	15.2	55.8	04 01	15 54	
290	17	W	28	10 47 43	15.1	55.3	06 14	16 07	NOTES
291	18	Th	29	11 30 45	15.0	54.9	06 28	16 22	Moon's G.H.A. and Dec. are given on page 3:69.
292	19	F	01	12 15 46	14.9	54.6	07 41	16 39	A table for correcting Moonrise and Moonset for latitude is on page 4:20.
293	20	Sa	02	13 01 46	14.8	54.3	08 54	17 01	A table for correcting Moon's meridian passage (transit) for longitude is on page 4:19.
294	21	Sun	03	13 50 49	14.7	54.1	10 04	17 30	Examples on the use of the above data are given on page 2:11 onwards.
295	22	M	04	14 39 49	14.7	54.0	11 07	18 09	
296	23	Tu	05	15 30 50	14.7	54.1	12 02	18 58	
297	24	W	06	16 20 49	14.8	54.3	12 45	19 58	
298	25	Th	07	17 09 48	14.9	54.6	13 19	21 07	
299	26	F	08	17 57 47	15.0	55.1	13 44	22 20	
300	27	Sa	09	18 44 46	15.2	55.8	14 04	23 35	
301	28	Sun	10	19 30 46	15.4	56.6	14 20	—	
302	29	M	11	20 16 46	15.7	57.5	14 35	00 52	
303	30	Tu	12	21 02 50	15.9	58.5	14 49	02 11	
304	31	W	13	21 52 52	16.2	59.4	15 04	03 33	

0h. = midnight. For explanation of use of above data see page 2:11 onwards.

MAY, 1990   3:35

0h. G.M.T. MAY 1   ★ ★   **STARS**   ★ ★   **0h. G.M.T. MAY 1**

No.	Name	Mag.	Transit (approx.)	DEC.	G.H.A.	R.A.	S.H.A.
			h. m.	° ′	° ′	h. m.	° ′
♈	ARIES	–	09 24	–	218 39.9	–	–
1	Alpheratz	2.2	09 31	N29 02.1	216 41.7	0 07	358 01.8
2	Ankaa	2.4	09 49	S42 21.3	212 12.8	0 25	353 32.9
3	Schedar	2.5	10 03	N56 28.9	208 40.9	0 39	350 01.0
4	Diphda	2.2	10 07	S18 02.3	207 53.3	0 43	349 13.4
5	Achernar	0.6	11 01	S57 16.9	194 19.8	1 37	335 39.9
6	POLARIS	2.1	11 44	N89 13.3	183 39.8	2 20	324 59.9
7	Hamal	2.2	11 31	N23 25.0	187 00.6	2 07	328 20.7
8	Acamar	3.1	12 22	S40 20.5	174 11.7	2 58	315 31.8
9	Menkar	2.8	12 25	N 4 03.2	173 13.4	3 01	314 33.5
10	Mirfak	1.9	12 47	N49 49.7	167 45.8	3 23	309 05.9
11	Aldebaran	1.1	13 59	N16 29.5	149 49.5	4 35	291 09.6
12	Rigel	0.3	14 38	S 8 12.7	140 08.9	5 14	281 29.0
13	Capella	0.2	14 39	N45 59.5	139 40.4	5 15	281 00.5
14	Bellatrix	1.7	14 48	N 6 20.5	137 30.8	5 24	278 50.9
15	Elnath	1.8	14 49	N28 36.1	137 14.8	5 25	278 34.9
16	Alnilam	1.8	14 59	S 1 12.4	134 44.1	5 35	276 04.2
17	Betelgeuse	{0.1 / 1.2}	15 18	N 7 24.4	130 00.2	5 54	271 20.3
18	Canopus	–0.9	15 47	S52 41.5	122 44.2	6 23	264 04.3
19	Sirius	–1.6	16 08	S16 42.2	117 29.1	6 44	258 49.2
20	Adhara	1.6	16 22	S28 57.6	114 06.3	6 58	255 26.4
21	Castor	1.6	16 57	N31 54.7	105 10.1	7 33	246 30.2
22	Procyon	0.5	17 03	N 5 15.0	103 57.9	7 39	245 18.0
23	Pollux	1.2	17 08	N28 03.1	102 28.9	7 44	243 49.0
24	Avior	1.7	17 46	S59 29.0	93 05.4	8 22	234 25.5
25	Suhail	2.2	18 31	S43 23.9	81 45.3	9 07	223 05.4
26	Miaplacidus	1.8	18 37	S69 41.0	80 23.7	9 13	221 43.8
27	Alphard	2.2	18 51	S 8 37.1	76 53.1	9 27	218 13.2
28	Regulus	1.3	19 31	N12 00.8	66 41.8	10 07	208 01.9
29	Dubhe	2.0	20 27	N61 48.4	52 52.2	11 03	194 12.3
30	Denebola	2.2	21 12	N14 37.5	41 31.0	11 48	182 51.1
31	Gienah	2.8	21 39	S17 29.5	34 49.9	12 15	176 10.0
32	Acrux	1.1	21 50	S63 03.1	32 08.5	12 26	173 28.6
33	Gacrux	1.6	21 54	S57 03.9	31 00.0	12 30	172 20.1
34	Mimosa	1.5	22 11	S59 38.5	26 52.1	12 47	168 12.2
35	Alioth	1.7	22 17	N56 00.8	25 15.1	12 53	166 35.2
36	Spica	1.2	22 48	S11 06.9	17 29.2	13 24	158 49.3
37	Alkaid	1.9	23 11	N49 21.6	11 51.8	13 47	153 11.9
38	Hadar	0.9	23 27	S60 19.9	7 52.1	14 03	149 12.2
39	Menkent	2.3	23 29	S36 19.6	7 07.7	14 05	148 27.8
40	Arcturus	0.2	23 39	N19 13.8	4 51.1	14 15	146 11.2
41	Rigil Kent	0.1	00 07	S60 48.0	358 54.9	14 39	140 15.0
42	Zuben'ubi	2.9	00 18	S16 00.4	356 04.2	14 50	137 24.3
43	Kochab	2.2	00 19	N74 11.6	355 57.6	14 51	137 17.7
44	Alphecca	2.3	01 02	N26 44.6	345 06.2	15 34	126 25.3
45	Antares	1.2	01 56	S26 24.8	331 27.1	16 28	112 47.2
46	Atria	1.9	02 15	S69 00.7	326 44.1	16 47	108 04.2
47	Sabik	2.6	02 37	S15 43.0	321 12.0	17 09	102 32.1
48	Shaula	1.7	03 00	S37 05.9	315 25.0	17 32	96 45.1
49	Rasalhague	2.1	03 02	N12 33.8	315 02.1	17 34	96 22.2
50	Eltanin	2.4	03 24	N51 29.1	309 33.6	17 56	90 53.7
51	Kaus Aust	2.0	03 51	S34 23.4	302 46.4	18 23	84 06.5
52	Vega	0.1	04 04	N38 46.2	299 30.3	18 36	80 50.4
53	Nunki	2.1	04 22	S26 18.6	294 59.4	18 54	76 19.5
54	Altair	0.9	05 17	N 8 50.4	281 04.9	19 49	62 25.0
55	Peacock	2.1	05 52	S56 45.8	272 26.0	20 24	53 46.1
56	Deneb	1.3	06 09	N45 14.4	268 23.2	20 41	49 43.3
57	Enif	2.5	07 11	N 9 49.7	252 44.1	21 43	34 04.2
58	Al Na'ir	2.2	07 35	S47 00.3	246 45.2	22 07	28 05.3
59	Fomalhaut	1.3	08 25	S29 40.3	234 23.0	22 57	15 43.1
60	Markab	2.6	08 32	N15 09.1	232 35.7	23 04	13 55.8

Stars Transit Correction Table

D. of Mth.	Corr. (Sub.)	D. of Mth.	Corr. (Sub.)
	h. m.		h. m.
1	–0 00	17	–1 03
2	–0 04	18	–1 07
3	–0 08	19	–1 11
4	–0 12	20	–1 15
5	–0 16	21	–1 19
6	–0 20	22	–1 23
7	–0 24	23	–1 27
8	–0 28	24	–1 30
9	–0 31	25	–1 34
10	–0 35	26	–1 38
11	–0 39	27	–1 42
12	–0 43	28	–1 46
13	–0 47	29	–1 50
14	–0 51	30	–1 54
15	–0 55	31	–1 58
16	–0 59		

STAR'S TRANSIT

To find the approx. time of Transit of a Star for any day of the month use above table.

If the quantity taken from the table is greater than the time of Transit for the first of the month, add 23h. 56min. to the time of transit before subtracting the correction below.

Example: The time is 1900h. on May 11th. What stars would be suitable for a Meridian altitude sight within the next hour, latitude 40°N.

	h.min.
Present time	19 00
Corr. for 11th	+00 39
Transit on May 1st	19 39
	+01 00
	20 39

Required a star Dec. N. Transit between 1939h. and 2039h. Answer: Dubhe (No 29) only.

MAY DIARY

d.	h.	
1	20	First Quarter
4	00	Mercury in inferior conjunction
5	02	Saturn stationary
9	20	Full Moon
10	00	Moon at apogee
11	13	Antares 0°.2S of Moon Occn.
15	08	Saturn 1°.5N of Moon
16	07	Mercury stationary
17	20	Last Quarter
19	20	Mars 6°S of Moon
21	20	Venus 7°S of Moon
23	03	Mercury 9°S of Moon
24	03	Moon at perigee
24	12	New Moon
27	02	Jupiter 2°S of Moon
31	03	Mercury greatest elong. W.(25°)
31	08	First Quarter

STAR TIME

The best time to take Star observations is shown in the a.m. and p.m. TWILIGHT columns on the opposite page — corrected for Latitude.

For Lighting-up Time (ashore) add 30 mins to Sunset Times.

For Star's G.H.A. Correction Table, see page 4:8.

For Alphabetical List of Stars with Constellation names, see page 2:24.

For Examples on the use of the above data, see page 2:11.

For full directions for finding the above 60 Stars, see p. 2:20 onwards. For Special Pole Star tables see pages 5:17-5:19.

OCTOBER, 1990   3:65

0h. G.M.T. OCTOBER 1 ★ ★ STARS ★ ★ 0h. G.M.T. OCTOBER 1

No.	Name	Mag.	Transit (approx.) h. m.	DEC. ° '	G.H.A. ° '	R.A. h. m.	S.H.A. ° '
♈	ARIES	—	23 18	—	9 28.1	—	—
1	Alpheratz	2.2	23 25	N29 02.6	7 29.0	0 07	358 00.9
2	Ankaa	2.4	23 43	S42 21.2	3 00.0	0 25	353 31.9
3	Schedar	2.5	23 57	N56 29.5	359 27.7	0 39	349 59.6
4	Diphda	2.2	00 05	S18 02.0	358 40.6	0 43	349 12.5
5	Achernar	0.6	00 59	S57 16.8	345 06.6	1 37	335 38.5
6	POLARIS	2.1	01 45	N89 13.5	333 36.7	2 23	324 08.6
7	Hamal	2.2	01 29	N23 25.4	337 47.8	2 07	328 19.7
8	Acamar	3.1	02 20	S40 20.2	324 58.8	2 58	315 30.7
9	Menkar	2.8	02 23	N 4 03.5	324 00.6	3 01	314 32.5
10	Mirfak	1.9	02 45	N49 49.8	318 32.5	3 23	309 04.4
11	Aldebaran	1.1	03 57	N16 29.7	300 36.8	4 35	291 08.7
12	Rigel	0.3	04 36	S 8 12.4	290 56.3	5 14	281 28.2
13	Capella	0.2	04 37	N45 59.4	290 27.4	5 15	280 59.3
14	Bellatrix	1.7	04 46	N 6 20.7	288 18.2	5 24	278 50.1
15	Elnath	1.8	04 47	N28 36.1	288 02.0	5 25	278 33.9
16	Alnilam	1.8	04 57	S 1 12.2	285 31.6	5 35	276 03.5
17	Betelgeuse	[0.1/1.2]	05 16	N 7 24.5	280 47.7	5 54	271 19.6
18	Canopus	-0.9	05 45	S52 41.0	273 31.6	6 23	264 03.5
19	Sirius	-1.6	06 06	S16 41.9	268 16.7	6 44	258 48.6
20	Adhara	1.6	06 20	S28 57.2	264 53.9	6 58	255 25.8
21	Castor	1.6	06 55	N31 54.5	255 57.6	7 33	246 29.5
22	Procyon	0.5	07 01	N 5 15.1	254 45.6	7 39	245 17.5
23	Pollux	1.2	07 06	N28 02.9	253 16.5	7 44	243 48.4
24	Avior	1.7	07 44	S59 28.4	243 53.3	8 22	234 25.2
25	Suhail	2.2	08 29	S43 23.4	232 33.3	9 07	223 05.2
26	Miaplacidus	1.8	08 35	S69 40.4	231 12.1	9 13	221 44.0
27	Alphard	2.2	08 49	S 8 37.0	227 41.0	9 27	218 12.0
28	Regulus	1.3	09 29	N12 00.8	217 29.8	10 07	208 01.7
29	Dubhe	2.0	10 25	N61 47.9	203 40.7	11 03	194 12.6
30	Denebola	2.2	11 10	N14 37.4	192 19.3	11 48	182 51.2
31	Gienah	2.8	11 37	S17 29.4	185 38.3	12 15	176 10.2
32	Acrux	1.1	11 48	S63 02.8	182 57.4	12 26	173 29.3
33	Gacrux	1.6	11 52	S57 03.7	181 48.8	12 30	172 20.7
34	Mimosa	1.5	12 09	S59 38.3	177 41.0	12 47	168 12.9
35	Alioth	1.7	12 15	N56 00.5	176 04.0	12 53	166 35.9
36	Spica	1.2	12 46	S11 06.8	168 17.6	13 24	158 49.5
37	Alkaid	1.9	13 09	N49 21.5	162 40.7	13 47	153 12.6
38	Hadar	0.9	13 25	S60 19.8	158 41.1	14 03	149 13.0
39	Menkent	2.3	13 27	S36 19.5	157 56.2	14 05	148 28.1
40	Arcturus	0.2	13 37	N19 13.8	155 39.6	14 15	146 11.5
41	Rigil Kent	0.1	14 01	S60 47.9	149 43.9	14 39	140 15.8
42	Zuben'ubi	2.9	14 12	S16 00.3	146 52.7	14 50	137 24.6
43	Kochab	2.2	14 13	N74 11.6	146 48.1	14 51	137 20.0
44	Alphecca	2.3	14 56	N26 44.8	135 53.7	15 34	126 25.6
45	Antares	1.2	15 50	S26 24.8	122 18.5	16 28	112 47.4
46	Atria	1.9	16 09	S69 01.0	117 33.1	16 47	108 05.0
47	Sabik	2.6	16 31	S15 42.9	112 00.3	17 09	102 32.2
48	Shaula	1.7	16 54	S37 06.0	106 13.3	17 32	96 45.2
49	Rasalhague	2.1	16 56	N12 34.1	105 50.5	17 34	96 22.4
50	Eltanin	2.4	17 18	N51 29.6	100 22.3	17 56	90 54.2
51	Kaus Aust.	2.0	17 45	S34 23.5	93 34.5	18 23	84 06.4
52	Vega	0.1	17 58	N38 46.7	90 18.7	18 36	80 50.6
53	Nunki	2.1	18 16	S26 18.6	85 47.5	18 54	76 19.4
54	Altair	0.9	19 11	N 8 50.7	71 52.9	19 49	62 24.8
55	Peacock	2.1	19 46	S56 46.1	63 13.7	20 24	53 45.6
56	Deneb	1.3	20 03	N45 15.1	59 11.1	20 41	49 43.0
57	Enif	2.5	21 06	N 9 50.1	43 31.7	21 43	34 03.6
58	Al Na'ir	2.2	21 29	S47 00.4	37 32.6	22 07	28 04.5
59	Fomalhaut	1.3	22 19	S29 40.2	25 10.4	22 57	15 42.3
60	Markab	2.6	22 26	N15 09.6	23 23.1	23 04	13 55.0

Stars Transit Correction Table

D. of Mth.	Corr. (Sub.) h. m.	D. of Mth.	Corr. (Sub.) h. m.
1	-0 00	17	-1 03
2	-0 04	18	-1 07
3	-0 08	19	-1 11
4	-0 12	20	-1 15
5	-0 16	21	-1 19
6	-0 20	22	-1 23
7	-0 24	23	-1 27
8	-0 28	24	-1 30
9	-0 31	25	-1 34
10	-0 35	26	-1 38
11	-0 39	27	-1 42
12	-0 43	28	-1 46
13	-0 47	29	-1 50
14	-0 51	30	-1 54
15	-0 55	31	-1 58
16	-0 59		

STAR'S TRANSIT

To find the approx. time of Transit of a Star for any day of the month use above table.

If the quantity taken from the table is greater than the time of Transit for the first of the month, add 23h. 56min. to the time of transit before subtracting the correction below.

Example: It is 0130h. on October 15th. How soon will you be able to get a Meridian altitude sight, and of which star?

```
                                h.min.
Present time .................. 01 30
Corr. for the 15th ......... +00 55
Corresponding time
on the 1st .................... 02 25
```

Answer: 20 min. Mirfak (No 10).

d. h. OCTOBER DIARY

```
 4 12 Full Moon
 6 18 Moon at perigee
 8 19 Mars 5°S of Moon
11 04 Last Quarter
12 20 Jupiter 1°N of Moon
                        Occn.
18 16 New Moon
20 12 Mars stationary
22 04 Mercury in superior
      conjunction
22 08 Antares 0°.6S of Moon
                        Occn.
22 16 Moon at apogee
25 17 Saturn 1°.1N of Moon
                        Occn.
26 20 First Quarter
```

STAR TIME

The best time to take Star observations is shown in the a.m. and p.m. TWILIGHT columns on the opposite page — corrected for Latitude.

For Lighting-up Time (ashore) add 30 mins to Sunset Times.

For Star's G.H.A. Correction Table, see page 4:8.

For Alphabetical List of Stars with Constellation names, see page 2:24.

For Examples on the use of the above data, see page 2:11.

For full directions for finding the above 60 Stars, see p. 2:20 onwards. For Special Pole Star tables see pages 5:17-5:19.

STAR OR PLANET ALTITUDE TOTAL CORRECTION TABLE

Always Subtractive (–)

Height of Eye above the Sea. Top line metres – lower line feet

Obs. Alt.	1.5	3	4.6	6	7.6	9	10.7	12	13.7	15	16.8	18	21.3
	5	10	15	20	25	30	35	40	45	50	55	60	70
9°	8.0	8.9	9.6	10.3	10.7	11.2	11.6	12.0	12.4	12.8	13.1	13.5	14.1
10°	7.4	8.4	9.1	9.7	10.2	10.6	11.1	11.5	11.8	12.2	12.5	12.9	13.5
11°	7.0	7.9	8.6	9.2	9.7	10.2	10.6	11.0	11.4	11.8	12.0	12.4	13.0
12°	6.6	7.5	8.2	8.8	9.3	9.8	10.2	10.6	11.0	11.4	11.6	12.0	12.6
13°	6.2	7.2	7.9	8.4	9.0	9.4	9.9	10.3	10.6	11.0	11.3	11.6	12.3
14°	5.9	6.9	7 6	8.1	8.6	9.2	9.6	10.0	10.3	10.7	11.0	11.3	12.0
15°	5.7	6.6	7.3	7.9	8.4	8.9	9.3	9.7	10.1	10.4	10.8	11.1	11.7
16°	5.5	6.4	7.1	7.7	8.2	8.7	9.1	9.5	9.9	10.2	10.5	10.9	11.5
17°	5.3	6.2	6.9	7.5	8.0	8.5	8.9	9.3	9.7	10.0	10.3	10.7	11.3
18°	5.1	6.0	6.7	7.3	7.8	8.3	8.7	9.1	9.5	9.8	10.2	10.5	11.1
19°	4.9	5.8	6.5	7.1	7.6	8.1	8.5	8.9	9.3	9.7	10.0	10.3	11.0
20°	4.8	5.7	6.4	7.0	7.5	8.0	8.4	8.8	9.2	9.6	9.9	10.2	10.8
25°	4.2	5.1	5.8	6.4	6.9	7 4	7.8	8.2	8.6	9.0	9.3	9.6	10.2
30°	3.8	4.7	5.4	6.0	6.5	7.0	7.4	7.8	8.2	8.6	8.9	9.2	9.8
35°	3.5	4.4	5.1	5.7	6.3	6.7	7.2	7.6	7.9	8.3	8.6	8.9	9.5
40°	3.3	4.2	4.9	5.5	6.0	6.5	6.9	7.3	7.7	8.1	8.4	8.7	9.3
50°	3.0	3.9	4.6	5.2	5.7	6.2	6.6	7.0	7.4	7.7	8.1	8.4	9.0
60°	2.7	3.6	4.4	4.9	5.5	5.9	6.4	6.8	7.1	7.5	7.8	8.1	8.8
70°	2.5	3.4	4.1	4.7	5.3	5.7	6.2	6.6	6.9	7.3	7.6	7.9	8.6
80°	2.3	3.3	4.0	4.6	5.1	5.5	6.0	6.4	6.7	7.1	7.4	7.8	8.4
90°	2.2	3.1	3.8	4.4	4.9	5.4	5.8	6.2	6.6	6.9	7.3	7.6	8.2

LAT 39°N

LHA	Hc Zn	Hc Zn	Hc Zn	Hc Zn	Hc Zn	Hc Zn	Hc Zn
	Dubhe	Regulus	PROCYON	SIRIUS	RIGEL	ALDEBARAN	Mirfak
120	33 59 019	34 32 099	50 53 125	31 35 201	29 06 229	40 14 258	59 19 297
121	34 14 019	35 18 100	51 31 126	31 17 202	28 31 230	39 28 259	58 38 297
122	34 30 019	36 04 101	52 09 127	30 59 203	27 55 230	38 43 260	57 56 297
123	34 45 019	36 50 102	52 45 129	30 40 204	27 19 231	37 57 260	57 14 297
124	35 00 019	37 35 102	53 22 130	30 21 205	26 42 232	37 11 261	56 33 297
125	35 15 019	38 21 103	53 57 131	30 00 207	26 05 233	36 25 262	55 51 297
126	35 31 019	39 06 104	54 32 132	29 39 208	25 28 234	35 38 262	55 10 297
127	35 46 020	39 52 105	55 06 134	29 17 209	24 50 235	34 52 263	54 28 297
128	36 02 020	40 37 105	55 39 135	28 54 210	24 11 236	34 06 264	53 47 297
129	36 18 020	41 21 106	56 12 137	28 31 211	23 33 236	33 19 265	53 06 298
130	36 33 020	42 06 107	56 43 138	28 07 212	22 54 237	32 33 265	52 24 298
131	36 49 020	42 51 108	57 14 140	27 42 213	22 14 238	31 47 266	51 43 298
132	37 05 020	43 35 109	57 43 141	27 17 214	21 35 239	31 00 267	51 02 298
133	37 21 020	44 19 110	58 12 143	26 51 214	20 55 240	30 13 267	50 21 298
134	37 37 020	45 03 111	58 40 145	26 24 215	20 14 240	29 27 268	49 40 298
	Kochab	◆ARCTURUS	SPICA	REGULUS	◆SIRIUS	BETELGEUSE	◆CAPELLA
135	37 53 020	20 29 081	10 46 114	59 06 146	25 57 216	37 49 245	48 59 299
136	38 09 020	21 15 082	11 29 115	59 31 148	25 29 217	37 07 246	48 18 299
137	38 25 020	22 01 083	12 11 115	59 56 150	25 00 218	36 24 247	47 37 299
138	38 42 020	22 47 083	12 53 116	60 18 152	24 31 219	35 41 248	46 56 299
139	38 58 020	23 34 084	13 35 117	60 40 153	24 01 220	34 57 249	46 16 299
140	39 14 020	24 20 084	14 16 118	61 00 155	23 31 221	34 14 249	45 35 300
141	39 30 020	25 06 085	14 57 118	61 19 157	23 00 222	33 30 250	44 55 300
142	39 47 020	25 53 086	15 38 119	61 36 159	22 29 223	32 46 251	44 14 300
143	40 03 020	26 39 086	16 19 120	61 52 161	21 57 224	32 02 252	43 34 300
144	40 19 021	27 26 087	16 59 120	62 06 163	21 25 224	31 17 253	42 54 301
145	40 36 021	28 12 087	17 39 121	62 19 165	20 52 225	30 33 253	42 14 301
146	40 52 021	28 59 088	18 19 122	62 30 167	20 19 226	29 48 254	41 34 301
147	41 08 021	29 46 089	18 59 123	62 40 169	19 45 227	29 03 255	40 54 302
148	41 25 021	30 32 089	19 38 124	62 47 172	19 11 228	28 18 256	40 14 302
149	41 41 020	31 19 090	20 16 124	62 53 174	18 36 228	27 33 256	39 35 302
	◆Kochab	ARCTURUS	◆SPICA	REGULUS	PROCYON	◆POLLUX	CAPELLA
150	41 57 020	32 05 090	20 55 125	62 58 176	43 34 233	59 58 259	38 55 302
151	42 14 020	32 52 091	21 33 126	63 00 178	42 56 234	59 12 260	38 16 303
152	42 30 020	33 39 092	22 10 127	63 01 180	42 19 235	58 26 261	37 37 303
153	42 46 020	34 25 092	22 47 128	63 00 182	41 40 236	57 40 261	36 58 303
154	43 02 020	35 12 093	23 24 128	62 57 184	41 02 237	56 54 262	36 19 304
155	43 18 020	35 58 094	24 01 129	62 53 187	40 22 238	56 08 263	35 40 304
156	43 35 020	36 45 094	24 36 130	62 47 189	39 43 239	55 21 264	35 02 304
157	43 51 020	37 31 095	25 12 131	62 39 191	39 03 240	54 35 265	34 23 305
158	44 07 020	38 18 096	25 47 132	62 29 193	38 22 241	53 48 265	33 45 305
159	44 23 020	39 04 096	26 21 133	62 18 195	37 41 242	53 02 266	33 07 305
160	44 38 020	39 51 097	26 55 134	62 05 197	37 00 242	52 15 267	32 29 306
161	44 54 020	40 37 098	27 29 134	61 51 199	36 19 243	51 29 267	31 51 306
162	45 10 020	41 23 099	28 02 135	61 35 201	35 37 244	50 42 268	31 13 306
163	45 26 020	42 09 099	28 34 136	61 17 203	34 55 245	49 56 269	30 36 307
164	45 41 019	42 55 100	29 06 137	60 59 205	34 12 246	49 09 269	29 58 307

LAT 39°N

LHA ♈	Hc	Zn	Hc	Zn	Hc	Zn	Hc	Zn	Hc	Zn	Hc	Zn	Hc	Zn
	♦Alpheratz		ALTAIR		Nunki		♦ANTARES		ARCTURUS		♦Alkaid		Kochab	
270	16 23	066	51 01	133	23 27	167	21 12	202	37 59	265	44 53	305	48 30	342
271	17 06	066	51 35	135	23 38	168	20 55	203	37 13	265	44 15	305	48 16	342
272	17 48	067	52 08	136	23 47	169	20 36	204	36 26	266	43 37	305	48 02	342
273	18 31	067	52 40	137	23 56	170	20 17	205	35 40	267	42 59	305	47 47	342
274	19 14	068	53 11	139	24 04	171	19 58	205	34 53	267	42 21	306	47 33	342
275	19 58	068	53 41	140	24 11	171	19 37	206	34 07	268	41 43	306	47 18	341
276	20 41	069	54 11	142	24 18	172	19 16	207	33 20	269	41 05	306	47 03	341
277	21 25	069	54 39	143	24 24	173	18 55	208	32 34	269	40 28	306	46 48	341
278	22 08	070	55 07	145	24 29	174	18 32	209	31 47	270	39 50	307	46 33	341
279	22 52	070	55 33	146	24 33	175	18 09	210	31 00	270	39 13	307	46 18	341
280	23 36	071	55 59	148	24 36	176	17 46	211	30 14	271	38 35	307	46 02	341
281	24 20	071	56 23	149	24 39	177	17 22	211	29 27	272	37 58	307	45 47	341
282	25 05	072	56 46	151	24 40	178	16 57	212	28 40	272	37 21	308	45 31	340
283	25 49	072	57 08	153	24 41	179	16 32	213	27 54	273	36 44	308	45 16	340
284	26 33	073	57 29	154	24 41	180	16 06	214	27 07	274	36 08	308	45 00	340
	♦Alpheratz		Enif		ALTAIR		♦Rasalhague		ARCTURUS		Alkaid		♦Kochab	
285	27 18	073	43 19	117	57 48	156	57 29	221	26 21	274	35 31	308	44 44	340
286	28 03	074	44 00	118	58 06	158	56 58	223	25 34	275	34 55	309	44 28	340
287	28 48	074	44 41	119	58 23	160	56 25	224	24 48	275	34 18	309	44 12	340
288	29 33	075	45 21	120	58 39	162	55 52	226	24 01	276	33 42	309	43 56	340
289	30 18	076	46 01	122	58 53	163	55 19	227	23 15	277	33 06	310	43 40	340
290	31 03	076	46 41	123	59 05	165	54 44	229	22 29	277	32 30	310	43 24	340
291	31 48	077	47 20	124	59 16	167	54 08	230	21 43	278	31 55	310	43 08	340
292	32 34	077	47 58	125	59 26	169	53 32	231	20 56	278	31 19	311	42 52	340
293	33 19	078	48 36	126	59 34	171	52 56	233	20 10	279	30 44	311	42 36	340
294	34 05	078	49 14	127	59 40	173	52 18	234	19 24	279	30 09	311	42 19	340
295	34 50	079	49 51	128	59 45	175	51 40	235	18 38	280	29 34	312	42 03	340
296	35 36	079	50 27	129	59 49	177	51 02	236	17 52	281	28 59	312	41 47	340
297	36 22	080	51 03	131	59 50	179	50 23	237	17 07	281	28 24	312	41 31	340
298	37 08	080	51 38	132	59 50	181	49 43	238	16 21	282	27 50	313	41 14	339
299	37 54	081	52 12	133	59 49	183	49 03	240	15 35	282	27 16	313	40 58	339
	♦Mirfak		Alpheratz		♦Enif		ALTAIR		Rasalhague		♦Alphecca		Kochab	
300	17 35	039	38 40	081	52 46	135	59 46	185	48 23	241	34 06	279	40 42	339
301	18 04	040	39 26	082	53 18	136	59 41	187	47 42	242	33 20	279	40 25	339
302	18 34	040	40 12	082	53 50	137	59 35	189	47 01	243	32 34	280	40 09	340
303	19 04	041	40 58	083	54 22	139	59 27	191	46 19	244	31 48	280	39 53	340
304	19 35	041	41 45	083	54 52	140	59 18	193	45 37	245	31 02	281	39 36	340
305	20 05	041	42 31	084	55 21	142	59 07	194	44 55	246	30 17	281	39 20	340
306	20 36	042	43 18	085	55 50	143	58 55	196	44 12	247	29 31	282	39 04	340
307	21 08	042	44 04	085	56 17	145	58 41	198	43 29	248	28 45	282	38 47	340
308	21 39	043	44 50	086	56 43	146	58 26	200	42 46	248	28 00	283	38 31	340
309	22 11	043	45 37	086	57 08	148	58 09	202	42 03	249	27 15	284	38 15	340
310	22 43	043	46 23	087	57 33	150	57 51	204	41 19	250	26 29	284	37 59	340
311	23 15	044	47 10	087	57 55	151	57 32	205	40 35	251	25 44	285	37 43	340
312	23 47	044	47 57	088	58 17	153	57 11	207	39 51	252	24 59	285	37 27	340
313	24 20	045	48 43	089	58 37	155	56 49	209	39 06	253	24 14	286	37 11	340
314	24 54	045	49 30	089	58 57	157	56 26	210	38 22	254	23 29	286	36 55	340

LAT 39°S

LHA ♈	Hc	Zn	Hc	Zn	Hc	Zn	Hc	Zn	Hc	Zn	Hc	Zn	Hc	Zn
	PROCYON		REGULUS		♦Suhail		ACRUX		♦ACHERNAR		RIGEL		♦BETELGEUSE	
90	40 12	033	13 05	062	54 54	113	31 24	148	44 38	224	57 32	338	43 35	358
91	40 37	032	13 46	062	55 37	112	31 49	148	44 06	224	57 14	337	43 33	357
92	41 01	031	14 27	061	56 20	112	32 14	148	43 34	224	56 55	335	43 29	355
93	41 25	029	15 07	060	57 03	112	32 38	147	43 01	224	56 35	333	43 25	354
94	41 47	028	15 48	060	57 47	112	33 04	147	42 29	223	56 13	332	43 20	353
95	42 09	027	16 28	059	58 30	112	33 29	147	41 57	223	55 50	330	43 13	351
96	42 29	026	17 08	058	59 13	112	33 54	147	41 25	223	55 26	328	43 06	350
97	42 49	024	17 47	057	59 57	111	34 20	147	40 54	223	55 01	327	42 57	349
98	43 08	023	18 26	056	60 40	111	34 45	147	40 22	223	54 35	325	42 47	347
99	43 26	022	19 05	056	61 23	111	35 11	146	39 50	223	54 08	324	42 37	346
100	43 42	020	19 43	055	62 07	111	35 37	146	39 19	223	53 40	322	42 25	345
101	43 58	019	20 21	054	62 50	111	36 03	146	38 47	222	53 11	321	42 12	343
102	44 13	018	20 59	053	63 34	111	36 29	146	38 16	222	52 41	319	41 58	342
103	44 27	016	21 36	053	64 18	111	36 55	146	37 44	222	52 11	318	41 43	341
104	44 39	015	22 13	052	65 01	111	37 22	146	37 13	222	51 39	317	41 28	340
	PROCYON		REGULUS		♦Gienah		ACRUX		♦ACHERNAR		RIGEL		♦BETELGEUSE	
105	44 51	014	22 49	051	19 26	097	37 48	145	36 42	222	51 07	315	41 11	338
106	45 01	012	23 25	050	20 13	097	38 15	145	36 11	221	50 33	314	40 53	337
107	45 11	011	24 00	049	20 59	096	38 41	145	35 40	221	50 00	313	40 34	336
108	45 19	010	24 35	048	21 45	095	39 08	145	35 10	221	49 25	312	40 15	335
109	45 26	008	25 10	047	22 32	095	39 35	145	34 39	221	48 50	310	39 54	333
110	45 32	007	25 44	047	23 18	094	40 02	145	34 09	221	48 14	309	39 33	332
111	45 37	005	26 18	046	24 05	094	40 28	145	33 38	220	47 37	308	39 11	331
112	45 41	004	26 51	045	24 51	093	40 55	145	33 08	220	47 00	307	38 47	330
113	45 43	002	27 23	044	25 38	092	41 22	145	32 38	220	46 23	306	38 23	329
114	45 45	001	27 55	043	26 25	092	41 49	145	32 08	220	45 45	305	37 59	327
115	45 45	000	28 27	042	27 11	091	42 16	144	31 39	219	45 06	304	37 33	326
116	45 44	358	28 58	041	27 58	090	42 44	144	31 09	219	44 27	302	37 07	325
117	45 42	357	29 28	040	28 44	090	43 11	144	30 40	219	43 47	301	36 40	324
118	45 39	355	29 58	039	29 31	089	43 38	144	30 11	219	43 07	300	36 12	323
119	45 34	354	30 27	038	30 18	089	44 05	144	29 42	218	42 27	299	35 44	322

5°	6°	7°	8°	9°	10°	11°	12°	13°	14°	
37 02 +43 118	37 45 +43 117	38 28 +43 116	39 11 +42 115	39 53 +42 115	40 35 +41 114	41 16 +40 113	41 56 +41 112	42 37 +39 111	43 16 +39 110	315
36 21 43 117	37 04 42 116	37 46 43 115	38 29 41 115	39 10 42 114	39 52 41 113	40 33 40 112	41 13 40 111	41 53 39 110	42 32 39 109	314
35 39 43 116	36 22 42 115	37 04 42 115	37 46 42 114	38 28 41 113	39 09 40 112	39 49 40 111	40 29 40 110	41 09 39 109	41 48 39 108	313
34 57 43 115	35 40 42 115	36 22 41 114	37 03 41 113	37 44 41 112	38 25 40 111	39 05 40 110	39 45 40 109	40 25 38 108	41 03 39 107	312
34 15 42 115	34 57 42 114	35 39 41 113	36 20 41 112	37 01 40 111	37 41 40 110	38 21 40 109	39 01 39 108	39 40 39 107	40 19 38 106	311
33 32 +42 114	34 14 +42 113	34 56 +41 112	35 37 +40 111	36 17 +41 110	36 58 +39 109	37 37 +40 108	38 17 +39 107	38 56 +38 106	39 34 +38 105	310
32 49 42 113	33 31 41 112	34 12 41 111	34 53 40 110	35 33 40 109	36 13 40 108	36 53 39 108	37 32 39 107	38 11 38 106	38 49 38 105	309
32 06 42 112	32 48 41 111	33 29 40 110	34 09 40 109	34 49 40 109	35 29 39 108	36 08 39 107	36 47 39 106	37 26 38 105	38 04 37 104	308
31 23 41 111	32 04 41 110	32 45 40 110	33 25 40 109	34 05 40 108	34 45 39 107	35 24 38 106	36 02 39 105	36 41 37 104	37 18 38 103	307
30 40 40 111	31 20 41 110	32 01 40 109	32 41 40 108	33 21 39 107	34 00 39 106	34 39 38 105	35 17 38 104	35 55 38 103	36 33 37 102	306
29 56 +40 110	30 36 +40 109	31 16 +40 108	31 56 +40 107	32 36 +39 106	33 15 +39 105	33 54 +38 104	34 32 +38 103	35 10 +37 103	35 47 +37 102	305
29 12 40 109	29 52 40 108	30 32 40 107	31 12 39 106	31 51 39 105	32 30 38 105	33 08 39 104	33 47 37 103	34 24 37 102	35 01 37 101	304
28 27 41 108	29 08 39 107	29 47 38 106	30 27 39 106	31 06 39 105	31 45 38 104	32 23 38 103	33 01 37 102	33 38 38 101	34 16 36 100	303
27 43 40 107	28 23 40 107	29 03 39 106	29 42 39 105	30 21 38 104	30 59 38 103	31 37 38 102	32 15 38 101	32 53 37 100	33 30 36 99	302
26 58 40 107	27 38 40 106	28 18 39 105	28 57 38 104	29 35 39 103	30 14 38 102	30 52 37 101	31 29 38 101	32 07 37 100	32 44 36 99	301
26 14 +39 106	26 53 +39 105	27 32 +39 104	28 11 +39 103	28 50 +38 103	29 28 +38 102	30 06 +38 101	30 44 +37 100	31 21 +36 99	31 57 +37 98	300
25 29 39 105	26 08 39 104	26 47 39 104	27 26 38 103	28 04 38 102	28 42 38 101	29 20 38 100	29 58 37 99	30 35 36 98	31 11 36 97	299
24 44 39 104	25 23 39 104	26 02 38 103	26 40 39 102	27 19 38 101	27 57 37 100	28 34 37 99	29 11 37 98	29 48 37 98	30 25 36 97	298
23 58 40 103	24 38 38 103	25 16 39 102	25 55 38 101	26 33 38 100	27 11 37 100	27 48 37 99	28 25 37 98	29 02 37 97	29 39 36 96	297
23 13 39 103	23 52 39 102	24 31 38 101	25 09 38 101	25 47 38 100	26 25 37 99	27 02 37 98	27 39 37 97	28 16 36 96	28 52 36 95	296
22 28 +38 102	23 06 +39 102	23 45 +38 101	24 23 +38 100	25 01 +37 99	25 38 +38 98	26 16 +37 97	26 53 +36 96	27 29 +37 96	28 06 +36 95	295
21 42 39 102	22 21 38 101	22 59 38 100	23 37 38 99	24 15 37 98	24 52 37 97	25 29 37 97	26 06 37 96	26 43 36 95	27 19 36 94	294
20 56 39 101	21 35 38 100	22 13 38 99	22 51 38 98	23 29 37 98	24 06 37 97	24 43 37 96	25 20 36 95	25 56 37 94	26 33 36 93	293
20 10 39 100	20 49 38 99	21 27 38 99	22 05 37 98	22 42 38 97	23 20 37 96	23 57 36 95	24 33 37 94	25 10 36 94	25 46 36 93	292
19 25 38 100	20 03 38 99	20 41 38 98	21 19 37 97	21 56 37 96	22 33 37 95	23 10 37 95	23 47 36 94	24 23 37 93	25 00 35 92	291

DECLINATION (0°-14°) SAME NAME AS LATITUDE

DECLINATION (15°–29°) SAME NAME AS LATITUDE

Each cell: Hc (° ′) d-correction, Z.

Lat	15°	19°	20°	21°	22°	26°	27°	28°	29°
45	43 55 +39 109	46 26 +35 104	47 01 +36 103	47 37 +34 102	48 11 +34 101	50 20 +30 101	50 50 +29 95	51 19 +28 93	51 47 +27 91 / 315
46	43 11 +38 108	45 40 +36 103	46 16 +35 102	46 51 +34 101	47 25 +33 100	49 34 +30 100	50 04 +29 95	50 33 +28 92	51 01 +27 91 / 314
47	42 27 +38 107	44 55 +35 103	45 30 +35 101	46 05 +34 100	46 39 +33 99	48 47 +29 99	49 17 +29 94	49 46 +28 91	50 14 +27 90 / 313
48	41 42 +37 106	44 09 +35 102	44 44 +35 101	45 19 +34 99	45 53 +33 98	48 01 +29 98	48 30 +29 93	48 59 +28 91	49 27 +27 89 / 312
49	40 57 +37 105	43 23 +36 101	43 59 +34 100	44 33 +34 99	45 07 +33 98	47 14 +30 98	47 44 +29 93	48 13 +28 90	48 41 +27 89 / 311
50	40 12 +37 104	42 38 +35 100	43 13 +34 99	43 47 +33 98	44 20 +33 97	46 27 +30 97	46 57 +29 92	47 26 +28 89	47 54 +27 88 / 310
51	39 27 +37 104	41 52 +34 99	42 26 +35 98	43 01 +33 97	43 34 +32 96	45 41 +30 96	46 11 +29 91	46 40 +28 89	47 08 +27 87 / 309
52	38 41 +37 103	41 06 +34 99	41 40 +34 98	42 14 +34 97	42 48 +32 95	44 54 +30 95	45 24 +29 91	45 53 +28 88	46 21 +27 87 / 308
53	37 56 +36 102	40 19 +35 98	40 54 +34 97	41 28 +33 96	42 01 +33 95	44 08 +29 95	44 37 +29 90	45 06 +28 88	45 35 +27 86 / 307
54	37 10 +37 101	39 33 +35 98	40 08 +34 96	40 42 +33 95	41 15 +33 94	43 21 +30 94	43 51 +29 89	44 20 +28 87	44 48 +27 86 / 306
55	36 24 +37 101	38 47 +34 97	39 21 +34 95	39 55 +33 95	40 28 +33 93	42 34 +30 93	43 04 +29 89	43 33 +29 86	44 02 +27 85 / 305
56	35 38 +37 100	38 01 +34 96	38 35 +34 95	39 09 +33 95	39 42 +32 93	41 48 +30 93	42 18 +29 88	42 47 +28 86	43 15 +28 85 / 304
57	34 52 +36 99	37 14 +34 95	37 48 +34 94	38 22 +33 94	38 55 +33 92	41 01 +30 92	41 31 +29 88	42 00 +29 85	42 29 +27 84 / 303
58	34 06 +36 98	36 28 +34 94	37 02 +33 93	37 35 +33 93	38 08 +33 92	40 15 +30 91	40 45 +29 87	41 14 +28 85	41 42 +28 84 / 302
59	33 20 +36 98	35 41 +34 94	36 15 +34 93	36 49 +33 93	37 22 +32 92	39 28 +30 91	39 58 +29 86	40 27 +29 84	40 56 +28 83 / 301
60	32 34 +36 97	34 55 +34 93	35 29 +33 92	36 02 +33 92	36 35 +33 91	38 42 +30 90	39 12 +29 86	39 41 +29 84	40 10 +28 82 / 300
61	31 47 +36 96	34 08 +34 92	34 42 +34 92	35 16 +33 91	35 49 +32 90	37 55 +30 89	38 25 +29 85	38 55 +29 83	39 24 +28 82 / 299
62	31 01 +36 96	33 21 +34 92	33 55 +34 91	34 29 +33 91	35 02 +32 90	37 09 +30 89	37 39 +29 85	38 08 +29 82	38 37 +29 81 / 298
63	30 15 +35 95	32 35 +34 91	33 09 +33 91	33 42 +33 91	34 14 +32 89	36 22 +31 88	36 53 +30 85	37 22 +29 82	37 51 +29 81 / 297
64	29 28 +36 94	31 48 +34 91	32 22 +34 91	32 56 +33 90	33 29 +32 89	35 36 +30 88	36 06 +30 84	36 36 +29 81	37 05 +29 80 / 296
65	28 42 +35 94	31 02 +34 90	31 36 +33 90	32 09 +33 89	32 42 +33 88	34 50 +30 87	35 20 +30 83	35 50 +30 81	36 20 +28 80 / 295
66	27 55 +36 93	30 15 +34 89	30 49 +34 89	31 23 +33 88	31 56 +32 87	34 03 +31 86	34 34 +30 82	35 04 +30 80	35 34 +29 79 / 294
67	27 09 +35 92	29 28 +34 89	30 02 +34 89	30 36 +34 88	31 09 +32 87	33 17 +31 86	33 48 +30 82	34 18 +30 80	34 48 +29 79 / 293
68	26 22 +35 92	28 42 +34 88	29 16 +33 88	29 49 +34 87	30 23 +32 86	32 31 +31 85	33 02 +30 81	33 32 +30 79	34 02 +30 78 / 292
69	25 35 +36 91	27 55 +34 87	28 29 +34 87	29 03 +33 87	29 36 +33 86	31 45 +31 85	32 16 +31 81	32 47 +30 79	33 17 +29 78 / 291

DECLINATION (15°-29°) **SAME** NAME AS LATITUDE

LAT 39°

HA	15° Hc	d	Z	16° Hc	d	Z	17° Hc	d	Z	18° Hc	d	Z	19° Hc	d	Z	20° Hc	d	Z	21° Hc	d	Z	22° Hc	d	Z	23° Hc	d	Z	24° Hc	d
70	2449 +35	90	2524 +35	90	2559 +35	89	2634 +35	88	2709 +35	87	2743 +33	86	2816 +34	85	2850 +34	84	2923 +32	83	2955 +32	83	2927 +38
71	2402	90	2438	89	2513	88	2548	87	2622	86	2656	85	2730	85	2803	84	2836	83	2909	82
72	2315	89	2351	89	2426	88	2501	87	2536	85	2610	84	2644	84	2717	83	2750	82	2823	32
73	2229	89	2304	88	2340	87	2414	85	2449	84	2523	84	2557	83	2631	82	2704	32	2737	32
74	2142	88	2218	87	2253	35	2328	35	2403	34	2437	34	2511	33	2545	33	2618	33	2651	33
75	2056 +35	87	2131 +34	86	2207 +35	85	2242 +34	84	2316 +35	84	2425 +34	82	2459 +33	82	2532 +33	80	2605 +33
76	2009	87	2045	86	2120	85	2155	84	2230	83	2304	82	2339	81	2413	81	2446	80	2519
77	1923	86	1958	86	2034	84	2109	84	2144	83	2218	82	2253	81	2327	79	2400	79	2434
78	1836	86	1912	85	1947	84	2022	83	2057	82	2132	81	2207	80	2241	79	2315	79	2348
79	1750	85	1825	35	1901	83	1936	35	2011	81	2046	81	2121	80	2155	79	2229	33	2303
80	1703 +34	83	1739 +34	84	1815 +35	83	1850 +35	81	1925 +35	80	2000 +34	80	2035 +34	78	2058 +34	77	2217 +34
81	1617	82	1653	35	1728	82	1804	35	1839	79	1914	79	1949	79	2024	78	2058	76	2212
82	1530	82	1606	35	1642	81	1718	35	1753	79	1828	79	1903	77	1938	76	1927	76	2047
83	1444	82	1520	36	1556	36	1632	35	1707	36	1743	35	1818	35	1855	35	1842	76	2002
84	1358	81	1434	36	1510	35	1546	36	1622	35	1657	35	1732	35	1807	35	1917	75	1917
85	1312 +36	81	1348 +36	80	1424 +36	80	1500 +36	79	1536 +36	78	1612 +36	76	1647 +35	76	1832 +35	75	1832 +35
86	1226	81	1302	37	1339	79	1415	36	1451	35	1526	36	1602	35	1637	35	1712	74	1747
87	1140	80	1216	37	1253	78	1329	36	1405	77	1441	36	1517	35	1552	35	1628	74	1703
88	1054	79	1131	37	1207	77	1244	37	1320	77	1356	36	1432	35	1507	35	1543	73	1618
89	1008 +37	79	1045	37	1122	77	1158 +37	76	1235	36	1311	75	1347	35	1423	35	1458	72	1534
90	0922 +37	78	0959 +37	77	1036 +37	77	1113 +37	75	1149 +37	75	1226 +36	74	1302 +36	73	1338 +36	72	1414 +35	72	1450 +35
91	0837	78	0914	37	0951	37	1028	37	1104	75	1141	74	1217	73	1254	36	1330	71	1406
92	0751	77	0829	38	0906	37	0943	37	1020	74	1056	73	1133	73	1210	36	1246	70	1322
93	0706	76	0743	38	0821	37	0858	37	0935	73	1012	73	1049	72	1126	36	1202	70	1238
94	0621	76	0658	38	0736	74	0813	37	0850	73	0927	72	1004	71	1041	36	1118	70	1155
95	0536 +37	75	0613 +38	74	0651 +37	73	0728 +38	72	0806 +37	72	0843 +37	71	0920 +36	70	0958 +37	69	1035 +37	69	1112 +37
96	0451	37	0528	38	0606	73	0644	38	0721	72	0759	71	0837	70	0914	37	0951	68	1028
97	0406	36	0444	38	0522	72	0600	38	0637	71	0715	70	0753	37	0830	37	0908	68	0945
98	0321	38	0359	38	0437	72	0515	38	0553	70	0631	70	0709	36	0747	36	0825	68	0903
99	0236	39	0315	38	0353	72	0431	39	0510	38	0548	69	0626	38	0704	36	0742	67	0820	38

154

LAT 39°

LHA	0° Hc	d	Z	1° Hc	d	Z	2° Hc	d	Z	3° Hc	d	Z	4° Hc	d	Z	13° Hc	d	Z	14° Hc	d	Z	LHA
69	1610	39	104	1531	40	104	1451	39	105	1412	40	106	1332	40	107	0728	41	113	0647	41	114	291
68	1656	40	104	1616	40	105	1536	40	106	1456	40	107	1416	40	107	0810	41	114	0729	41	115	292
67	1741	40	105	1701	40	106	1621	40	107	1541	41	107	1501	41	108	0853	42	115	0811	42	116	293
66	1826	40	106	1746	40	106	1706	41	107	1625	40	108	1545	41	108	0935	42	116	0853	42	116	294
65	1910	-40	106	1830	-40	107	1750	-40	108	1710	-41	109	1629	-41	109	1017	-42	116	0935	-42	117	295
64	1955	40	107	1915	41	108	1834	41	109	1754	41	109	1713	41	110	1059	42	117	1016	42	118	296
63	2040	41	108	1959	40	108	1919	41	109	1838	41	110	1757	42	111	1140	42	118	1058	43	118	297
62	2124	41	109	2043	41	109	2002	41	110	1921	41	111	1840	41	111	1221	43	119	1138	42	119	298
61	2208	41	109	2127	41	110	2046	41	111	2005	42	112	1923	41	112	1302	43	119	1219	43	120	299
60	2252	-41	110	2211	-41	110	2130	-42	112	2048	-42	112	2006	-42	113	1343	-44	120	1259	-43	120	300
59	2336	42	111	2254	41	112	2213	42	112	2131	42	113	2049	42	114	1423	43	120	1340	44	121	301
58	2419	41	112	2338	42	112	2256	42	113	2214	42	114	2132	43	114	1503	44	122	1419	44	122	302
57	2502	41	112	2421	42	113	2339	43	114	2256	42	115	2214	43	115	1543	44	122	1459	45	123	303
56	2546	43	113	2503	42	114	2421	42	115	2339	43	115	2256	43	116	1622	44	123	1538	45	123	304
55	2628	-42	114	2546	-43	115	2503	-42	115	2421	-43	116	2338	-44	117	1701	-45	123	1617	-45	124	305
54	2711	43	115	2628	43	115	2545	45	116	2502	43	117	2419	43	118	1740	45	124	1655	45	125	306
53	2753	43	115	2710	43	116	2627	43	117	2544	44	118	2500	44	118	1819	46	125	1733	46	126	307
52	2835	43	116	2752	43	117	2709	44	118	2625	44	119	2541	45	119	1857	46	126	1811	46	126	308
51	2917	44	117	2833	43	118	2750	44	119	2706	44	119	2622	45	120	1934	46	127	1848	46	127	309
50	2958	-44	118	2914	-44	119	2830	-44	119	2746	-44	120	2702	-45	121	2012	-47	127	1925	-46	128	310
49	3039	44	119	2955	44	120	2911	45	120	2826	44	121	2742	46	122	2048	46	128	2002	47	129	311
48	3120	44	120	3036	45	120	2951	45	121	2906	45	123	2821	45	123	2125	47	129	2038	47	130	312
47	3200	44	120	3116	45	121	3031	45	122	2946	46	123	2900	46	124	2201	47	130	2114	48	130	313
46	3240	45	121	3155	45	122	3110	46	123	3025	46	124	2939	46	124	2237	48	131	2149	48	131	314
45	3320	-45	122	3235	-46	122	3149	-46	124	3103	-46	125	3017	-46	125	2312	-49	131	2224	-49	132	315
44	3359	46	123	3314	46	124	3228	47	125	3141	46	126	3055	47	126	2347	49	132	2258	49	133	316
43	3438	46	124	3352	46	125	3306	47	126	3219	47	126	3132	47	127	2421	49	133	2332	49	134	317
42	3517	47	125	3430	46	126	3344	47	127	3257	48	127	3209	47	128	2455	50	134	2405	49	135	318
41	3555	47	126	3508	47	127	3421	47	127	3334	48	128	3246	48	129	2528	50	135	2438	50	136	319
40	3632	-47	127	3545	-47	128	3458	-48	128	3410	-48	129	3322	-48	130	2601	-50	136	2511	-51	136	320

DECLINATION (0°-14°) **CONTRARY** NAME AS LATITUDE

NAVIGATION TABLE 18: CORR TO TAB ALTITUDE

a / ′	1	2	3	4	5	6	7	8	9	10	11	12	13	14	15	16	17	18	19	20	21	22	23	24	25	26	27	28	29	30
0	0	0	0	0	0	0	0	0	0	0	0	0	0	0	0	0	0	0	0	0	0	0	0	0	0	0	0	0	0	0
1	0	0	0	0	0	0	0	0	0	0	0	0	0	0	0	0	0	0	0	0	0	0	0	0	0	0	0	0	0	0
2	0	0	0	0	0	0	0	0	0	0	0	0	0	0	0	1	1	1	1	1	1	1	1	1	1	1	1	1	1	1
3	0	0	0	0	0	0	0	0	0	0	1	1	1	1	1	1	1	1	1	1	1	1	1	1	1	1	1	1	1	2
4	0	0	0	0	0	0	0	1	1	1	1	1	1	1	1	1	1	1	1	1	1	1	2	2	2	2	2	2	2	2
5	0	0	0	0	0	0	1	1	1	1	1	1	1	1	1	1	1	2	2	2	2	2	2	2	2	2	2	2	2	2
6	0	0	0	0	0	1	1	1	1	1	1	1	1	1	2	2	2	2	2	2	2	2	2	2	2	3	3	3	3	3
7	0	0	0	0	1	1	1	1	1	1	1	1	2	2	2	2	2	2	2	2	2	3	3	3	3	3	3	3	3	4
8	0	0	0	1	1	1	1	1	1	1	1	2	2	2	2	2	2	2	3	3	3	3	3	3	3	3	4	4	4	4
9	0	0	0	1	1	1	1	1	1	2	2	2	2	2	2	2	3	3	3	3	3	3	3	4	4	4	4	4	4	4
10	0	0	0	1	1	1	1	1	2	2	2	2	2	2	2	3	3	3	3	3	4	4	4	4	4	4	4	5	5	5
11	0	0	1	1	1	1	1	1	2	2	2	2	2	3	3	3	3	3	3	4	4	4	4	4	5	5	5	5	5	6
12	0	0	1	1	1	1	1	2	2	2	2	2	3	3	3	3	3	4	4	4	4	4	5	5	5	5	5	6	6	6
13	0	0	1	1	1	1	2	2	2	2	2	3	3	3	3	3	4	4	4	4	5	5	5	5	5	6	6	6	6	6
14	0	0	1	1	1	1	2	2	2	2	3	3	3	3	4	4	4	4	4	5	5	5	5	6	6	6	6	7	7	7
15	0	0	1	1	1	2	2	2	2	2	3	3	3	4	4	4	4	4	5	5	5	6	6	6	6	6	7	7	7	8
16	0	1	1	1	1	2	2	2	2	3	3	3	3	4	4	4	5	5	5	5	6	6	6	6	7	7	7	7	8	8
17	0	1	1	1	1	2	2	2	3	3	3	3	4	4	4	5	5	5	5	6	6	6	7	7	7	7	8	8	8	8
18	0	1	1	1	2	2	2	2	3	3	3	4	4	4	4	5	5	5	6	6	6	7	7	7	8	8	8	8	9	9
19	0	1	1	1	2	2	2	3	3	3	3	4	4	4	5	5	5	6	6	6	7	7	7	8	8	8	9	9	9	10
20	0	1	1	1	2	2	2	3	3	3	4	4	4	5	5	5	6	6	6	7	7	7	8	8	8	9	9	9	10	10
21	0	1	1	1	2	2	2	3	3	4	4	4	5	5	5	6	6	6	7	7	7	8	8	8	9	9	9	10	10	10
22	0	1	1	1	2	2	3	3	3	4	4	4	5	5	6	6	6	7	7	7	8	8	8	9	9	10	10	10	11	11
23	0	1	1	2	2	2	3	3	3	4	4	5	5	5	6	6	7	7	7	8	8	8	9	9	10	10	10	11	11	12
24	0	1	1	2	2	2	3	3	4	4	4	5	5	6	6	6	7	7	8	8	8	9	9	10	10	10	11	11	12	12
25	0	1	1	2	2	2	3	3	4	4	5	5	5	6	6	7	7	8	8	8	9	9	10	10	10	11	11	12	12	12
26	0	1	1	2	2	3	3	3	4	4	5	5	6	6	6	7	7	8	8	9	9	10	10	10	11	11	12	12	13	13
27	0	1	1	2	2	3	3	4	4	4	5	5	6	6	7	7	8	8	9	9	9	10	10	11	11	12	12	13	13	14
28	0	1	1	2	2	3	3	4	4	5	5	6	6	7	7	7	8	8	9	9	10	10	11	11	12	12	13	13	14	14
29	0	1	1	2	2	3	3	4	4	5	5	6	6	7	7	8	8	9	9	10	10	11	11	12	12	13	13	14	14	14
30	0	1	2	2	2	3	4	4	4	5	6	6	6	7	8	8	8	9	10	10	10	11	12	12	12	13	14	14	14	15
31	1	1	2	2	3	3	4	4	5	5	6	6	7	7	8	8	9	9	10	10	11	11	12	12	13	13	14	14	15	16
32	1	1	2	2	3	3	4	4	5	5	6	6	7	7	8	9	9	10	10	11	11	12	12	13	13	14	14	15	15	16
33	1	1	2	2	3	3	4	4	5	6	6	7	7	8	8	9	9	10	10	11	12	12	13	13	14	14	15	15	16	16
34	1	1	2	2	3	3	4	5	5	6	6	7	7	8	8	9	10	10	11	11	12	12	13	14	14	15	15	16	16	17
35	1	1	2	2	3	4	4	5	5	6	6	7	8	8	9	9	10	10	11	12	12	13	13	14	15	15	16	16	17	18
36	1	1	2	2	3	4	4	5	5	6	7	7	8	8	9	10	10	11	11	12	13	13	14	14	15	16	16	17	17	18
37	1	1	2	3	3	4	4	5	6	6	7	7	8	9	9	10	10	11	12	12	13	14	14	15	15	16	17	17	18	18
38	1	1	2	3	3	4	4	5	6	6	7	8	8	9	10	10	11	11	12	13	13	14	15	15	16	16	17	18	18	19
39	1	1	2	3	3	4	5	5	6	6	7	8	8	9	10	10	11	12	12	13	14	14	15	16	16	17	18	18	19	20
40	1	1	2	3	3	4	5	5	6	7	7	8	9	9	10	11	11	12	13	13	14	15	15	16	17	17	18	19	19	20
41	1	1	2	3	3	4	5	5	6	7	8	8	9	10	10	11	12	12	13	14	14	15	16	16	17	18	18	19	20	20
42	1	1	2	3	4	4	5	6	6	7	8	8	9	10	10	11	12	13	13	14	15	15	16	17	18	18	19	20	20	21
43	1	1	2	3	4	4	5	6	6	7	8	9	9	10	11	11	12	13	14	14	15	16	16	17	18	19	19	20	21	22
44	1	1	2	3	4	4	5	6	7	7	8	9	10	10	11	12	12	13	14	15	15	16	17	18	18	19	20	21	21	22
45	1	2	2	3	4	4	5	6	7	8	8	9	10	10	11	12	13	14	14	15	16	16	17	18	19	20	20	21	22	22
46	1	2	2	3	4	5	5	6	7	8	8	9	10	11	12	12	13	14	15	15	16	17	18	18	19	20	21	21	22	23
47	1	2	2	3	4	5	5	6	7	8	9	9	10	11	12	13	13	14	15	16	16	17	18	19	20	20	21	22	23	24
48	1	2	2	3	4	5	6	6	7	8	9	10	10	11	12	13	14	14	15	16	17	18	18	19	20	21	22	22	23	24
49	1	2	2	3	4	5	6	7	7	8	9	10	11	11	12	13	14	15	16	16	17	18	19	20	20	21	22	23	24	24
50	1	2	2	3	4	5	6	7	8	8	9	10	11	12	12	13	14	15	16	17	18	18	19	20	21	22	22	23	24	25
51	1	2	3	3	4	5	6	7	8	8	9	10	11	12	13	14	14	15	16	17	18	19	20	20	21	22	23	24	25	26
52	1	2	3	3	4	5	6	7	8	9	10	10	11	12	13	14	15	16	16	17	18	19	20	21	22	23	23	24	25	26
53	1	2	3	4	4	5	6	7	8	9	10	11	11	12	13	14	15	16	17	18	19	19	20	21	22	23	24	25	26	27
54	1	2	3	4	4	5	6	7	8	9	10	11	12	13	14	14	15	16	17	18	19	20	21	22	22	23	24	25	26	27
55	1	2	3	4	5	6	6	7	8	9	10	11	12	13	14	15	16	16	17	18	19	20	21	22	23	24	25	26	27	28
56	1	2	3	4	5	6	7	7	8	9	10	11	12	13	14	15	16	17	18	19	20	21	21	22	23	24	25	26	27	28
57	1	2	3	4	5	6	7	8	9	10	11	12	13	14	14	15	16	17	18	19	20	21	22	23	24	25	26	27	28	29
58	1	2	3	4	5	6	7	8	9	10	11	12	13	14	14	15	16	17	18	19	20	21	22	23	24	25	26	27	28	29
59	1	2	3	4	5	6	7	8	9	10	11	12	13	14	15	16	17	18	19	20	21	22	23	24	25	26	27	28	29	30

31	32	33	34	35	36	37	38	39	40	41	42	43	44	45	46	47	48	49	50	51	52	53	54	55	56	57	58	59	60	$\frac{a}{'}$
0	0	0	0	0	0	0	0	0	0	0	0	0	0	0	0	0	0	0	0	0	0	0	0	0	0	0	0	0	0	0
1	1	1	1	1	1	1	1	1	1	1	1	1	1	1	1	1	1	1	1	1	1	1	1	1	1	1	1	1	1	1
1	1	1	1	1	1	1	1	1	1	1	1	1	1	2	2	2	2	2	2	2	2	2	2	2	2	2	2	2	2	2
2	2	2	2	2	2	2	2	2	2	2	2	2	2	2	2	2	2	2	2	3	3	3	3	3	3	3	3	3	3	3
2	2	2	2	2	2	2	3	3	3	3	3	3	3	3	3	3	3	3	3	3	3	4	4	4	4	4	4	4	4	4
3	3	3	3	3	3	3	3	3	3	3	4	4	4	4	4	4	4	4	4	4	4	4	4	5	5	5	5	5	5	5
3	3	3	3	4	4	4	4	4	4	4	4	4	4	4	5	5	5	5	5	5	5	5	5	6	6	6	6	6	6	6
4	4	4	4	4	4	4	4	5	5	5	5	5	5	5	6	6	6	6	6	6	6	6	6	6	7	7	7	7	7	7
4	4	4	5	5	5	5	5	5	5	6	6	6	6	6	6	6	6	7	7	7	7	7	7	7	7	8	8	8	8	8
5	5	5	5	5	5	6	6	6	6	6	6	6	7	7	7	7	7	7	8	8	8	8	8	8	8	9	9	9	9	9
5	5	6	6	6	6	6	6	6	7	7	7	7	7	8	8	8	8	8	8	8	9	9	9	9	9	10	10	10	10	10
6	6	6	6	6	7	7	7	7	7	8	8	8	8	8	8	9	9	9	9	9	10	10	10	10	10	10	11	11	11	11
6	6	7	7	7	7	7	8	8	8	8	8	9	9	9	9	9	10	10	10	10	10	11	11	11	11	11	12	12	12	12
7	7	7	7	8	8	8	8	8	9	9	9	9	10	10	10	10	10	11	11	11	11	11	12	12	12	12	13	13	13	13
7	7	8	8	8	8	9	9	9	9	10	10	10	10	10	11	11	11	11	12	12	12	12	13	13	13	13	14	14	14	14
8	8	8	8	9	9	9	10	10	10	10	10	11	11	11	12	12	12	12	12	13	13	13	14	14	14	14	14	15	15	15
8	9	9	9	9	10	10	10	10	11	11	11	11	12	12	12	13	13	13	13	14	14	14	14	15	15	15	15	16	16	16
9	9	9	10	10	10	10	11	11	11	12	12	12	12	12	13	13	13	14	14	14	14	15	15	15	16	16	16	17	17	17
9	10	10	10	10	11	11	11	12	12	12	13	13	13	14	14	14	14	15	15	15	16	16	16	16	17	17	17	18	18	18
10	10	10	11	11	11	12	12	12	13	13	13	14	14	14	15	15	15	16	16	16	16	17	17	17	18	18	18	19	19	19
10	11	11	11	12	12	12	13	13	13	14	14	14	15	15	15	16	16	16	17	17	17	18	18	18	19	19	19	20	20	20
11	11	11	12	12	12	13	13	13	14	14	14	15	15	15	16	16	17	17	18	18	18	19	19	19	20	20	20	21	21	21
11	11	12	12	13	13	13	14	14	14	15	15	16	16	16	17	17	18	18	18	19	19	19	20	20	20	21	21	22	22	22
11	12	12	13	13	13	14	14	14	15	15	15	16	17	17	17	18	18	19	19	20	20	20	21	21	21	22	22	23	23	23
12	13	13	13	14	14	15	15	15	16	16	16	17	17	18	18	19	19	20	20	20	21	21	22	22	22	23	23	24	24	24
13	13	14	14	15	15	15	16	16	17	17	18	18	18	19	19	20	20	20	21	21	22	22	22	23	23	24	24	25	25	25
13	14	14	15	15	16	16	16	17	17	18	18	19	19	20	20	20	21	21	22	22	23	23	23	24	24	25	25	26	26	26
14	14	15	15	16	16	17	17	17	18	18	19	19	20	20	21	21	22	22	22	23	23	24	24	25	25	26	26	27	27	27
14	15	15	16	16	17	17	18	18	19	19	20	20	21	21	22	23	23	24	24	25	25	26	26	27	27	28	28	28	28	28
15	15	16	16	17	17	18	18	19	19	20	20	21	21	22	23	23	24	24	25	25	26	27	27	27	28	28	29	29	29	29
16	16	16	17	18	18	18	19	20	20	20	21	22	22	22	23	24	24	24	25	26	26	26	27	28	28	28	29	30	30	30
16	17	17	18	18	19	19	20	20	21	21	22	22	23	23	24	25	25	26	27	27	27	28	28	29	30	30	31	31	32	31
17	17	17	18	19	19	20	20	21	21	22	22	23	23	24	25	25	26	26	27	27	28	28	29	29	30	30	31	31	32	32
17	18	18	19	19	20	20	21	21	22	23	23	24	24	25	25	26	26	27	28	28	29	29	30	30	31	31	32	32	33	33
18	18	18	19	20	20	21	22	22	23	23	24	24	25	26	26	27	27	28	28	29	30	30	31	31	32	32	33	33	34	34
18	19	19	20	20	21	22	22	23	23	24	24	25	26	26	27	27	28	29	29	30	30	31	32	32	33	33	34	34	35	35
19	19	20	20	21	22	22	23	23	24	25	25	26	26	27	28	28	29	29	30	31	31	32	32	33	34	34	35	35	36	36
19	20	20	21	22	22	23	23	24	25	25	26	26	27	28	28	29	29	30	31	31	32	33	33	34	35	35	36	36	37	37
20	20	21	21	22	23	23	24	25	25	26	27	27	28	28	29	30	30	31	32	32	33	34	34	35	35	36	37	37	38	38
20	21	21	22	23	23	24	25	25	26	27	27	28	29	29	30	31	31	32	32	33	34	34	35	36	36	37	38	38	39	39
21	21	22	23	23	24	25	25	26	27	27	28	29	29	30	31	31	32	33	33	34	35	35	36	37	37	38	39	39	40	40
21	22	22	23	23	24	25	26	27	27	28	29	30	30	31	31	32	33	33	34	35	36	36	37	38	38	39	40	40	41	41
22	22	23	24	24	25	26	27	27	28	29	29	30	31	32	32	33	34	34	35	36	36	37	38	38	39	40	41	41	42	42
22	23	24	24	25	26	26	27	28	29	29	30	31	32	32	33	34	34	35	36	37	37	38	39	40	40	41	42	42	43	43
23	23	24	25	25	26	27	28	28	29	30	31	32	32	33	34	34	35	36	37	37	38	39	40	40	41	42	43	43	44	44
23	24	24	26	26	27	28	28	29	30	31	32	32	33	34	34	35	36	37	38	38	39	40	40	41	42	42	44	44	45	45
24	25	25	26	27	28	28	29	30	31	31	32	33	34	34	35	36	37	38	38	39	40	41	41	42	43	44	44	45	46	46
24	25	26	27	27	28	29	30	30	31	32	33	33	34	35	36	37	37	38	39	40	41	42	42	43	44	44	45	46	47	47
25	26	26	27	28	29	30	30	31	32	33	33	34	35	36	37	38	38	39	40	41	42	42	43	44	45	46	46	47	48	48
25	26	27	28	29	29	30	31	32	33	33	34	35	36	37	38	38	39	40	41	42	42	43	44	45	46	47	47	48	49	49
26	27	28	28	29	30	31	32	32	33	34	35	36	37	38	38	39	40	41	42	42	43	44	45	46	47	48	48	49	50	50
26	27	28	29	30	31	31	32	33	34	35	35	36	37	38	39	40	41	42	42	43	44	45	46	47	48	48	49	50	51	51
27	28	29	29	30	31	32	33	34	35	36	36	37	38	39	40	41	42	42	43	44	45	46	47	48	49	49	50	51	52	52
27	28	29	30	31	32	33	34	34	35	36	37	38	39	40	41	42	42	43	44	45	46	47	48	49	49	50	51	52	53	53
28	29	30	31	32	32	33	34	35	36	37	38	39	40	40	41	42	43	44	45	45	47	48	49	50	50	51	52	53	54	54
28	29	30	31	32	33	34	35	36	37	38	38	39	40	41	42	43	44	45	46	47	48	49	50	50	51	52	53	54	55	55
29	30	31	32	33	34	35	35	36	37	38	39	40	41	42	43	44	45	46	47	48	49	49	50	51	52	53	54	55	56	56
29	30	31	32	33	34	35	36	36	38	39	40	41	42	43	44	45	45	47	48	49	50	51	52	53	54	54	55	56	57	57
30	31	32	33	34	35	36	37	38	39	40	41	42	43	44	45	46	47	48	49	50	51	52	52	53	54	55	56	57	58	58
30	31	32	33	34	35	36	37	38	39	40	41	42	43	44	45	46	47	48	49	50	51	52	53	54	55	56	57	58	59	59

INDEX